YALE   MBIA   HARVARD   MT. ELBERT

COTTONWOOD CREEK

TURQUOISE LAKE

TWIN LAKES

LEADVILLE

TRAIN WRECK

ISTA

WALT FOX'S ACCIDENT

GRANITE

S. KNECHT

When a middle-aged, successful New York executive revisits the Colorado mining country of his youth during a summer vacation, some surprising things happen.

Such as deciding to rebuild the old family cabin high in the Rockies—and moving in for a spell.

Well, not quite a spell. For the rest of his life! After, of course, notifying his aghast New York business partners that he has embarked upon a new life.

As he roves the country around Leadville, Buena Vista, and even Denver, the memories of his turn-of-the-century youth flood back. But there are more than rich memories. The old families are still there, the children of the ranchers and miners and sheepmen he grew up with. And up in his cabin, over a tumbler of bourbon, in front of a roaring fire with a local newspaperman as a foil, the now reborn protagonist reflects on the course of the 20th century.

George Roche has not quite written fiction. The stories he recounts are real ones from the rich family trove that Roches have preserved for generations. Of course he has disguised a few to protect privacy, but essentially these captivating stories of early Colorado are true.

This lovely little book will enthrall young and old alike, and perhaps give new meaning to the old maxim that "you can't go home again."

GOING HOME

GOING HOME

George Roche

Jameson Books
Ottawa, IL

Jameson Books are available at special discounts for
bulk purchases for sales promotions, premiums,
fund-raising, or educational use. Special editions
can also be created to specification.

Jameson Books
722 Columbus Street
Ottawa, IL. 61350

(815) 434-7905

Distributed by Kampmann & Co., New York

**Library of Congress Cataloging-in-Publication
Data**

Roche, George Charles.
  Going home.

  I. Title.
PS3568.0323G6 1986   813'.54   86-3559
ISBN 0-915463-34-2

10 9 8 7 6 5 4 3 2 1

Printed in the United States of America
ISBN: 0-915463-34-2

To Jake

CONTENTS

FOREWORD

This is a delightful book, a memoir in form and fiction in method. Every time I use the word fiction I'm conscious of its inadequacy for the various arts of storytelling. What truly offends me is "prose fiction": prose indicates prosaic; fiction the opposite of truth. Both these words are in the vocabulary of poor English teachers or teachers who feel that verse is the only place for imagination. It seems a conspiracy of those who use abstract definitions to escape the discipline of reading. It is the same kind of mind that has segmented history into ancient, Medieval and modern. When is modern modern? Now, yesterday, day after tomorrow? Such a mind has the most curious understanding of Time. It is an evasive definition of a craft which makes the reader aware of his humanity, even in a way drama cannot. The definitions of prosody are clear, but not so fiction. I've tried to find the source of this inadequate definition for the other usage of the imagination of language. I looked to the Justinian code, where I found the word novel over and over again. There novel meant a law. The Spanish friars gave a clue. They called *Don Quixote* a lying history. As an aside, one might say that when priests judge by temporal means, the devil jigs.

A memoir is written in the first person. The point of view is confessional and is as old as *The Confessions of Saint Augustine*. Both a memoir and fiction have the same anecdotes, actions, and concrete instances, with this difference: in a story whatever makes up an action also exhibits an

9

enveloping action, which is the universal truth behind a particular presentation of the truth. In *Going Home* we have the hero, lost in the world of materialism, rejecting this to return to a cabin in the Rockies where he hopes to recover what he has lost. This presents the irony of the book, which is the common plight of all of us, even of those who do not understand what has taken place, and that is the damage to the common inheritance, a Christian belief in the divine order of the universe. Belief in this gave the freedom to accept and face all the opposites which present themselves as we work and play, love, raise families. Every man was some kind of craftsman, with his own tools, which gave him the right to refuse or accept an offer. How clear this is in *Going Home*, where the crafts were as dangerous and as hard as mining, or ranching, which at times can be as dangerous and demanding as mining, when for example a bewildering snowstorm in the high passes threatens the lives of man and animals. This phenomenon is one phase of the great diversity in nature's actions. It could be of cattle, hunting the doggies in blinding and frigid weather. In *Going Home* it happens to be sheep, and the reader is left with the sense that all were saved by divine intervention, which could not have happened if the shepherd had not as a matter of course taken his responsibility for the flock. Once safely down the mountain he didn't even report the peril he and his dog suffered with the sheep. Those who have dogs only for pets can never enjoy the absolute intimacy and trust of creaturehood between man and animal as this tale tells, for behind it, dim though it be, is the metaphysical intimacy all animals knew when they first appeared in the Garden of Innocence.

That men and women in our once free society knew their places and accepted their obligations in both public and private matters is one instance of the meaning of this book. As a child growing up in the far West the hero was not aware that Washington had anything to do with Denver. It was my experience in Murfreesboro, Tennessee. Coming home at first dark from play, I felt no danger, only an unconscious well-being. The only warning of any threat was the Gypsies who came through once a year to bury their dead in Nashville. The stealing of children was not much of a threat, for to a child the gypsy life had certain appeals. But that I might never see my family again was fearsome beyond words or, even, contemplation. But who could take seriously being stolen as I walked home and all along the street, from house to house, the smell of coffee roasting saturated the air. No savor could have been more comforting and reassuring, words at that time unknown to me. Every detail, incident and scene in *Going Home* makes clear what has been lost. Now we buy coffee in cans, already roasted but not to a particular taste or need. Most things come to us from afar. Little initiates itself at home. We are uprooted spiritually if not always physically. My grandmother Nelson at eighty-three died at the place where she was born. There are few farmers who can say they work the ground their fathers worked. There are few farmers. Agribusiness announces their demise. The saddest plight is that of the western farmers. They complain publicly of losing the family farm, but accepting themselves as only business creatures, that is, depending only on money and trades, reveals how ignorant they are of what has happened to them. For one thing, the family farm raises its own power in mules and horses, and its own fuel in corn and hay and clovers. No occupation dependent on the weather can survive depending only on Lady money, Sir Thomas More's words, in the shifting of what people worshipped.

It is appalling to think how fast the family in the Christian sense has disappeared. The general confusion resulting from the various bureaucracies in their efforts to

replace the familial authority can only compound itself.
Before this catastrophe every child, as this book so dra-
matically shows, knew that the parents held the final authority, with the grandmother as a court of appeals. I can
hear Mammy, my father's mother saying, "Quit fighting
the children and give them something to eat." It was she,
in that back room, who told you when to take off your
long winter underwear, and when you could go barefooted
in the spring. The grandmother in this book played a
larger role. She was widowed early by one of the dangers
of the West, forcing upon her a double part. She had to
make a living. She never complained of its hardships and
she never lost her faith in God. This she transmitted to the
boy, who loved and continually turned to her. In time the
boy turned to his grandfather for other instruction. In this
western life and in farm life everywhere the apprenticeship
is gradually learned, according to what the child can bear.
Perhaps the most wicked thing Washington has done is
defining a child only as a laborer, revoking parenthood
and love. Power, never love, is the secular grounds for
action in a servile state. This is Satanic.

If the grandmother stands for the moral and spiritual
instruction, the grandfather prepares the boy for the risks,
as well as the knowledge for what can only be his craft,
sometimes more than one. Under this tutelage go the skills
of mining, the saloon, which then was not just a place to
get a drink, but a kind of club where males could congre-
gate freely and refresh themselves, for a short while entirely free of feminine restraints.

Whatever the tensions between the sexes, the home was
the unit of our society, and generally the dwelling house
its location. The door was the symbol for the common life.
Behind it the woman rules in all domestic matters and at
times more than domestic. Beyond the door the man was
intended to take charge and make the living, vote, and

concern himself with those concerns which had to do with the family's welfare. This was so in Tennessee as it was in Colorado, before the Liberals began to move progressively toward an impossibility, the perfectibility of man. This is now the American dream, the ultimate fantasy. Down with God. Up with Man. Reading this book, one will learn how great is the loss when matter and reason so assert themselves as the only values.

*   *   *   *   *

Formerly in the void of night, after midnight, from the edge of silence comes the rooster's first crow; then an answer, until far and near the comforting calls and answers enter the silence like light. Today the endless void is all silence. There is no third crow. The denial is also silent.

Andrew Lytle
Monteagle, Tennessee

PREFACE

Most of the stories you are about to read are the stories of my family. At least four generations appear in these pages. Most of the names of people and places have their real-life counterparts.

One of the dearest possessions of this family has always been its privacy. I have respected that privacy. There were many other stories which I chose not to tell, not now at least. I have freely mixed the stories of different generations as yet another way to protect that privacy.

Still, the spirit of another time and place has been preserved in the story told here. This is a story with something to say about at least one part of our national experience and about some of those Americans who lived through it.

George Roche

I have eaten your bread and salt,
I have drunk your water and wine;
The deaths ye died I have watched beside
And the lives that ye led were mine.

Was there aught that I did not share
In vigil or toil or ease —
One joy or woe that I did not know,
Dear hearts across the seas?

I have written the tale of our life
For a sheltered people's mirth,
In jesting guise — but ye are wise,
And ye know what the jest is worth.

RUDYARD KIPLING

GOING HOME

I

HOMECOMING

Funny thing about mountains — I've lived around here for over half of my nearly eighty years. I think I know every rock and tree in the hills around the cabin. But the slightest change in the pattern of clouds overhead, the sudden descent of a little rain or mist, and the mood of the mountains is completely altered. The way the sun hits the high ridges in the first light, the deep shadows that begin to form in the hollows long before dusk — each change makes this little Gulch a different place, another world all its own.

Maybe the changes aren't in the mountains. Sometimes I think the changes are in me. I bring my own moods and ideas to the timeless face of these mountains, but the soaring heights of rock, the wind whispering in the pines, the sound of the creek rushing down the boulder-strewn path it cuts in the valley floor, take my thoughts and rework them, filling me with feelings that are still mine and yet somehow more than mine.

Does this sound like the musing and muttering of a crazy old man who has spent too much time alone? Could be. I like to think otherwise. I like to think that my Gulch is a special place, a place where a man can touch another existence beyond his own. I like to think I can ask my important questions and find my important answers right here.

I'm really not such a recluse. I've seen quite a bit of the world. It's just that I never found another place I liked as well. While most of the world has been changing, the Gulch somehow remains the same. The sameness gives me an anchor to remember other times and other places — and especially other people. Here I'm never really alone.

There was a time when like most kids I wanted to see the world. Lord knows, I did. I didn't decide to come home again until about twenty years ago. By then I'd made more than enough money, proved I could meet the world on its own terms, and decided that most of the people and places I'd been seeing lately weren't very interesting or satisfying. At fifty-eight I'd reached what the me-generation now calls the "existential crisis." I was beginning to suspect that I might not live forever after all. It's quite a shock when that idea first sinks in. I decided I must be missing something and that I'd better not wait any longer to go look for it.

Without quite knowing what I was looking for, or where I might find it, I told my people in the New York office that I was taking the summer off. I owned a big piece of the partnership and we were completing twenty years of great success, so nobody made it hard for me to carry out my whim. My partners couldn't see what was so important about my trip, but raised no real objection. I'd bought a little time to take a look at myself and my life.

Planes are faster, but somehow I didn't want to rush

things. By early June of that summer in 1960, a westward train trip of two thousand miles brought me into the Colorado town near where I used to live, in the Saguache mountains on the spine of the Rockies, one hundred miles south and west of Denver. The Gulch where I'd lived was still thirty miles away, straight back into the high country.

As I stepped off the train, my first feeling was curiosity. I needn't have bothered to wonder about the town — there weren't many changes. The yellow clapboard station, the row of old men soaking up the late afternoon summer sun along the edge of the platform, the smell of cinders strong in the air. Twenty years earlier I'd boarded another train in identical surroundings on that same platform.

I carried my bag past the station. My train was already moving along the tracks of the Denver and Rio Grande main line, heading north to Leadville. Standing at the point where the tracks cut the town in two, I looked up and down the main street of Buena Vista — not much new. There were more automobiles than twenty years ago, parked diagonally all down the street. There was a new drugstore. The Buena Vista Hotel had enjoyed a modest face lift. The Green Parrot saloon looked about the same, already doing a lively Friday night trade, with a few cowboys and townies lining the bar.

I stood there in the long twilight, bag in hand, enjoying the satisfaction of seeing the place and people so largely unchanged. So far I had seen no one I recognized, but the people of the town seemed the same, with their leathery, weather-beaten, open faces.

I decided to stay over until morning, especially since I'd need a ride out to the Gulch. As the lights in town winked on, I walked down the street, drawing the clean, clear air into my lungs and savoring the leisurely, unattached feeling that had come over me.

The elk head over the reception desk in the Buena Vista

Hotel looked down with benign disinterest as I took a room. My next stop was the hotel bar, a dark, cool, mahogany-paneled room adjoining the lobby. The bartender was a tall, angular middle-aged man who had been a tall, angular young man twenty years ago. I remembered him, but he seemed not to recognize me. He was a good deal less benign than the elk, and no more interested in my presence. The first Friday night customers were starting to arrive and business was picking up. I'd been in New York and Washington a long time, but I knew better than to order a martini in a shot-and-beer town. After the first round, the whiskey and beer left me with a warm spot that was a pleasant reminder of other times and places. I was enjoying my seat at the corner of the bar, watching the people and listening to the talk. One or two of those who came into the bar looked vaguely familiar, but no one showed more than passing interest in me. The bartender refilled my shot glass and placed a fresh Coors on the dark old mahogany bar. I grinned at the thought of some of my New York and Washington associates putting down a glass of Jim Beam and chasing it with a Coors.

Dinner in the hotel still didn't produce anyone who recognized me, though my young waitress looked remarkably like a girl I'd once known. Then it occurred to me that I was probably remembering the girl's mother.

I've always been a walker. After dinner I left the hotel and headed toward the river. The Arkansas at this point isn't large — its source is only forty miles to the north, near Leadville. On this June night, an early moon left its dancing pattern on the water as the Arkansas rushed on its way down a narrow valley between two mountain ranges. The last row of houses disappeared over the edge of the hill behind me as I walked down to the water. The stars were bright, with a clarity the night sky never achieves anywhere else. In this country, the night air has a chill even in June. Standing on the riverbank, I felt content to be in the hills. Whether I was feeling the contentment of a middle-aged businessman on a pleasant holiday, or the contentment of someone who was coming home again, I didn't know. Even now I'm not sure just what was taking hold of me.

I scrambled back up the hill to town and strolled the length of Main Street, across the tracks and on to the opposite edge of Buena Vista. Peering into the darkness beyond the lights of the last houses, I could feel the loom of the mountains jutting upward to frame the horizon around the little town. It was late when I hiked back to the hotel and bed. Half relieved and half disappointed that so far no one had recognized me, I finally realized that no one had really had a chance since I'd been careful to avoid any real contact since arriving in town. Homecoming had been uneventful, but I was going to bed filled with a curious joy, and an eagerness to begin the next day.

After breakfast the next morning, I stepped out into a brilliant day with the clear air and the bright sun of a summer morning in the high country. Buena Vista had a Saturday morning bustle. People in the hills get to town early on Saturday. Ranchers, farmers, townies, and kids were spread up and down the street, in and out of cars and pickups. The post office, grocery stores, hardware store, and drugstore were all doing plenty of business. The Green Parrot and the other saloons were still closed, but that was only because the liquor laws prohibited opening before noon. The bartenders were already sweeping out, preparing to open the doors for the thirsty rush of business that always follows a Saturday morning in town.

Heading straight for the office of the *Chaffee County Republican*, I was ready to get reacquainted with the town and the people. The paper was edited by Ed Gregg, a tough old warhorse of a country publisher who had been a good friend. I went sailing into the *Republican* office all set to renew acquaintance with my past — and maybe to show off a bit as hometown-boy-made-good. But now the changes began to show. Twenty years are twenty years. Sitting at Ed Gregg's battered old rolltop desk, behind the presses that crowded the room, was Ed's son, Gibby. He'd been a kid when I left town. Now a broad, powerful man in his middle forties, he sat in his dad's chair as though he belonged there.

And he did belong there. Gibby remembered me as soon as I spoke. When I asked about his father, he told me that Ed Gregg had been dead for fifteen years. Gibby had taken over when his father died, and for a time had been one of the younger newspaper editors in the United States. Running a newspaper, even a country weekly, would be a challenge for most youngsters, but not for Gibby. He had his father's big jaw and the same firm, quiet way of saying things so that you knew he meant them.

I spent most of the morning with Gibby and caught up on two decades. He was surprised and pleased when I told him I wanted to go up to see the old place in the Gulch. No one had lived there since I left and the place was so far up the Gulch that it had few visitors. Gibby wasn't even sure it was still standing, but he offered to spend the afternoon taking me out for a look.

Gibby and I made the rounds of Buena Vista to pick up food, cooking gear, sleeping bag, Levis, boots, flannel shirt, and a heavy coat. I also bought a 25-35 Remington at the hardware store — really too light for deer, but a nice little rifle to have around a camp. We stopped by the liquor store for a couple bottles and paid a brief visit to the Green Parrot. Every place we stopped now brought a welcome from people who remembered me, and I remembered most of them, though there were more new faces than I'd have guessed.

Loaded down like a dude on his first camping trip, I clambered into the jeep that Gibby kept for trips into the hills. By midafternoon we were on our way. As we bumped along over the corduroy patterns in the dirt road leading toward the Gulch, I leaned back to enjoy the fresh air, the open space, the clean sweep of the mountains high above us. We were paralleling the peaks, making our way across a high plateau that sloped from the mountains to the river, several miles below. From that plateau I could see miles of the country—the Arkansas running south, with a ridge of mountains on each side and watering the rich grassland that formed the heart of the ranches, spread out for miles before me on the valley floor.

The jeep labored to the head of the plateau and followed the winding road down into Chalk Creek Gulch. The great open spaces of the Arkansas Valley suddenly constricted into a long narrow gulch, flanked by even higher and craggier mountains, great granite walls rising almost perpendicular to the valley floor. We followed the stream bed westward, climbing higher and higher toward the continental divide. The Gulch grew steadily narrower, the country wilder. The jeep humped its way over a fainter and fainter excuse for a road as it growled into the high country, stopping at last when the road came to its absolute end.

Gibby turned off the ignition. "I still can't believe you want to stay up here alone. But at least you'll have gear and enough food to stay a couple of weeks. I'll drop up in a week or so and see how you're making out."

By the time the late darkness of June in the high country overtook us, we had climbed the last few feet of the trail to the old cabin. It was too dark to see much when we arrived, so we postponed a real investigation until Sunday morning.

One of the amiable features of a country editor's job,

I've since learned, is that a man who keeps up with his work can usually afford to close shop for a day or two whenever a good excuse comes along. Gibby had made arrangements to delay his return to town until Sunday afternoon, so I had a guest for my first night in camp.

The spring in the rocks behind the cabin was still flowing. The water was as sweet and cold as I remembered. The whiskey was warm and strong against the growing chill of the high country night. We built a fire and fixed a meal. Talking beside the fire to this powerful, quiet man with the dark, deep-set features, a man so like his father whom I had known and respected, made it seem as though I had never really been away. That night, lying fully clothed in my sleeping bag on a bed of pine boughs, looking up through the trees at the blaze of starlight above, I found myself looking forward to the summer.

Rolling out of a sleeping bag in the first light of a high country dawn is a bracing experience for a middle-aged businessman. Even in June there are likely to be little touches of frost here and there on the grass. A fire and a cup of coffee laced with whiskey soon had me warm. Gibby offered to fix breakfast while I climbed the hillside to the cabin. I think he knew I wanted to be alone when I first saw the place.

The roof was mostly gone. The cabin was still standing, but much the worse for wear. Twenty mountain winters had taken their toll with no one around to mend the damage. Forcing the door back over the warped floor boards, I heard the pack rats scurry for cover as I came in. Memories flooded back to me as I stepped over the rotting boards. The front room with its fireplace in one wall and the two smaller rooms in back still had a few furnishings. The mattress in the bedroom had provided a home for several generations of ten-stripes. The old kitchen table showed signs of visitation by all the birds in the neighborhood, but the stove looked usable. The root cellar in the hillside behind the cabin was still intact. There weren't many other signs to tell anything about the people who had lived there. Standing in the front door of the cabin, looking down to the floor of the Gulch and up to the sheer walls of granite rising on the other side, I realized that the condition of the cabin didn't really make any difference. The point of my memories was out there, in the ridge upon ridge of somber pine and bright aspen reaching up to the stark gray face of the mountains above timberline. The beauty and strength I saw somehow filled a void that had been lying unrecognized within me for years. As I stood there, the warmth of the morning sun was just beginning to reach toward the dark shadows on the Gulch floor, but the sun's rays were already transforming the higher slopes into pillars and ridges of fiery splendor. I'd come home again.

Gibby was on his way back to town by noon, leaving me to savor a June day in the high country. The afternoon brought the daily shower that comes to the mountains in summer, but the storm was gone as quickly as it had come, leaving me brilliant sunshine and blue sky to explore the area around camp. Here there were *no* changes. Time had stopped. Memory after memory flooded my mind as the afternoon progressed. Dark brought a campfire and dinner. Fresh air brought an early trip to bed, setting a pattern for every day of that first week. No real plans were taking shape, but I found myself profoundly at peace, enjoying the country and enjoying the privacy.

Each day took me a little farther afield. I climbed up through the newly leafed aspen and the pine, clambering over boulders and rock slides to reach timberline, sucking oxygen into my lungs as I paused for breath in the thin air. As I paused, I could hear the roar of the creek racing along its boulder-strewn path far below.

One day I followed the stream bed for several miles, locating the springs and the rivulets of melting snow from the mountains above as they added to the flow that would move twenty miles down Chalk Creek to the Arkansas, rushing onward in a greater and greater torrent until it left the mountains and began its slow, winding path south and east across the plains, eventually reaching the Mississippi and moving on to the Gulf of Mexico — all from the springs and snowmasses of the Colorado mountains.

Oh, those mountains! A few days up here and I began to understand all over again what the trappers and the westering pioneers in the wagon trains that followed must have felt when they first beheld the Rockies.

The geologists say it took three billion years to produce the world as we know it. The Book of Genesis says it took six days. Probably both versions are right — it all depends on how you measure your days. Whichever version a human being accepts requires a considerable act of faith. It just isn't possible for most of us to comprehend the enormousness and complexity of our world. We live in a tiny moment of space and time with no real understanding of what it's all about. Sometimes a few of us are lucky enough to push against the confines of our tiny, compartmentalized lives and discover a little more about the world and about ourselves. I believe that's what frontiers and mountains are all about.

The frontier spirit in America is associated in people's minds with the challenges of westward migration. The covered wagon has a place in our hearts. The mountain man seemed to challenge the high country for the sheer joy of the challenge. Somehow the pioneering spirit seemed to be most alive in a wilderness where beauty and strength went hand in hand.

Perhaps that's why the pioneers sensed that God and beauty, the Creator and His work, are very closely connected. One thing we know for sure: it's easy to understand that idea when you look out over range after range of rugged beauty in the Rocky Mountains. A gigantic granite roof extends north, south and west out of sight and almost out of imagination. Here the weather builds — thunder, lightning, rain, snow. Here these sentinels stand as they stood centuries before the first pioneer laid eyes on them. Here these same sentinels may well stand centuries after the last of us have gone our way.

As I stood there in my mountain valley with the country stretching away in its beauty, strength, and sheer size, it seemed a little easier, even for a middle-aged businessman, to understand the people who settled this country, people as tough as those trees standing just below timberline. Like those trees, they had to be tough to survive. Like those trees, the pioneers could look to the mountains and sense that somewhere up there the work of man comes to an end and the work of God continues.

The week went fast. Late the following Saturday, Gibby drove out from Buena Vista and huffed up the last hill to the camp, backpacking another week of pork and beans, sausage, steak, bacon, coffee, and assorted odds and ends, including another bottle of whiskey. We had a few shots, cooked the steaks over the open fire, and savored the night air.

"George, you seem to be enjoying yourself. How long do you plan to stay?"

"I don't have to be back in New York until September. The way this week rushed by, I'd like to stay in the Gulch all summer. What I'd really like to do is fix up the old cabin."

"Well, you've been paying the taxes all these years so it's yours to fix. Are you sure you want to put all that work into the old place? It'll take a lot of time and money."

"Gibby, I've got all summer. As for the money, I ought

to be able to afford an old mountain cabin. What do you think it might cost?"

"All told, a couple thousand dollars — if you do your own work."

"Somehow I'd like to do this one myself."

The next Monday morning, June 15, 1960, found me in the county seat. I had descended the Gulch with Gibby on Sunday night, staying over with his family in Buena Vista. The next morning I drove the twenty-five-mile trip down the Arkansas Valley to Salida in Gibby's car. *Salida* means "gateway" in Spanish and the name fits the town. All the way south from Buena Vista the mountains form a narrow channel for the Arkansas River and the ranches that dot the green pasture land on both sides of the stream. At Salida, ringed by rugged mountains on all sides, the valley seems to end, but the river escapes down a narrow winding canyon which a few miles farther southeast becomes the Royal Gorge. One leaves Salida over high passes: to the western slope over Monarch Pass, to the south into the open cattle country of the San Luis Valley. A gateway indeed.

The sun that June morning warmed Salida and warmed the front steps of the county courthouse as I entered the cool, dark interior. I made sure that the tax rolls were in order and confronted a clerk who couldn't believe anybody was really going to live in the old place. For some reason I couldn't explain; I was proud of myself. I was doing the right thing. The trip back to Buena Vista was a pleasure. Gibby and I had a couple of drinks at the Green Parrot and then adjourned to the Buena Vista Hotel for lunch. By dark that night I was the proud owner of a Dodge Power Wagon of an indeterminate World War II vintage. It ran and, most important, had the low gears, high clearance, and four-wheel drive to grind up the Gulch. Gibby spent Tuesday with me as we assembled lumber, paint, roofing, cement, a few sheets of glass, a collection of necessary tools, and everything else it seemed we might need. Late that afternoon he followed me up the Gulch to the point where the road quit. It took most of Wednesday to clear the boulders and fallen trees that blocked our last approach to the cabin, but Wednesday night saw the "road" completed and everything unloaded, with Gibby on his way back to town. I invited him to dinner, but he told me that even country editors had to work on occasion. We tossed off a drink straight from the bottle to christen the place and Gibby was on his way to set the type and write the copy for Friday's *Chaffee County Republican.* As the night closed in, I began to feel I was really home.

The days and weeks rushed by. The New York businessman was having the time of his life. The cabin took shape with each passing day. As the lumber, roofing, glass, and paint fell into place, I was proud of the progress, never prouder than the day the small cistern for the spring was completed behind the cabin. By early August the place was really taking shape. Gibby visited occasionally, now and then staying over a day to lend a hand. Once a week or sometimes every two weeks, I'd leave the Gulch, visit Buena Vista, have a good bath, a change of clothes, a good meal, and a night in a regular bed. The next morning I'd load the Power Wagon with a week's supplies and head back up the Gulch.

I grew tanned and *happy.* My life in New York drifted further away all the time. In the back of my mind, I suppose I always knew that fall and the "real" world were fast approaching, but the mountains and the cabin somehow seemed much more real.

By late summer, the reality of the Gulch was replacing the outside world in my thoughts. I began thinking about staying on for the fall. I found myself preparing the cabin for winter use — insulating, laying in firewood and supplies. At the time I didn't realize it, but the decision was already being made within me not to return to New York. I was beginning to think I had come home.

One Saturday in late August I made my usual trip to Buena Vista for supplies. Gibby and I drank away a good part of the afternoon as we discussed the future. With large holdings in mining properties and no real obligations, I finally faced the fact that I didn't need or want to go back to New York. Gibby warned me that living so far up the Gulch would be difficult when the snow flew, but he agreed that it could be done and he gradually got as excited as I was about the project. We closed the Green Parrot that night and I stayed over at the Buena Vista Hotel. The next morning I called New York from Gibby's office at the paper. When I told my partners that I'd be staying in Colorado through Christmas, the first reaction was disbelief. The next reaction was, "How the hell do you expect us to handle everything here?"

Then came the warning: "If you're not here damned fast, this is going to cost you a lot of money!"

I had been expecting that. "I've got plenty of money and you know it. See you next year." I slammed down the phone and shook hands with Gibby. As I drove out to the Gulch, gazing up at my enormous mountains in the haze of an early fall morning, I realized that I was already home. The decision was made.

Looking back to that fall in 1960, I now realize that until then I'd been drifting. Until that moment I was trapped in a pattern of living that had lost its point for me. At such moments, a man can be lost for good unless he finds something really to believe in, a dream to which he can give his whole heart. For me, that dream was waiting in my private mountain country. Twenty years of business life in the rush of wartime Washington and postwar New York had never really blunted the memory. We all have such dreams,

inconsolable secrets within each of us that can't be shared and yet can't really be hidden. For some, the dream may lie in the past. Others may yearn for an experience not yet arrived — news from a place never seen. Either way, not many of us ever act to reach our dreams. Perhaps most of us don't act because we're afraid to find that the dream may not really be there. I don't know.

I do know that I was lucky — I did reach out and my dream was there.

That first winter the dream grew steadily. The isolation of the deep mountain winter was seldom broken. Except for occasional trips to town to restock the supplies and spend an evening with Gibby and a few cronies at the Green Parrot, I was never out of the Gulch. The old Power Wagon was parked at the end of the graded road where the snowplow turned around, so my last mile, in and out, had to be handled on snowshoes. Believe me, that reduces trips to town.

The longer I stayed, the more I reveled in the choice I'd made. I loved the company of an occasional trip to Buena Vista. I loved the silence of a snowshoe trail over deep, glistening banks of snow in the clear, cold air. Most of all, I loved the crackle of the fire as the high-country storms swirled outside the cabin. It's always easy to be alone in bad weather.

By the fire, the memories flooded in — Grammaw Hagee, Grampa Stewart, Denver, Leadville, the Gulch. I remembered the ranchers, the miners, the bartenders, the schoolteachers — those and so many others I'd known. I rehearsed the stories Grammaw Hagee told me of homesteading days, the mining stories of Grampa Stewart.

I came to know another batch of characters and their stories in the years after I returned to live in the Gulch. The same independence, the same reason for living, was still there in the high country and its people. During the twenty years since my homecoming, the old stories and the new, my memories and the memories of others, have run together in a single stream. I've begun to see a pattern of people and events where time no longer plays a part. The past, the present, the mountains, and the people form a single tapestry.

The dreams of that first homecoming winter came back clearly and have grown sharper as the last twenty years have slipped past. Somewhere along the line I learned why this Gulch and its memories have such a hold on me. I expect you'll think I'm crazy, but I hope some may understand.

I have seen the face of God.

Perhaps to you that statement is sacrilegious. You're right to say that there's an infinite difference in quality between our purpose in time and God's purpose in eternity. I know Nature is mortal. I know you and I will outlive her. She's only an image, a symbol, a pale reflection of the Creator. But it's in that reflection that we focus our attention on God as well as on His creation. Stand where I've stood, see what I've seen, listen to that majestic silence — I believe you'll admit that we're in a special place. To be here is to stand before a Presence that makes time itself stand still.

No doubt other special places exist. No doubt those who know firsthand about such special places also realize they've seen God. Any who have experienced that Presence will know what I mean. Others have to continue their own search for the face of God. Rest assured, God shows a bit of Himself to anyone who's willing to understand what he sees. When God does show Himself to one of us, the chorus of voices always rises to cry that this cannot be, that such a vision is illogical. I say that when such a vision frees us from our self-imposed prison, we should seize that vision with all our heart. Illogical? Let logic find its own explanation for life. An infinite question is never fully resolved by a finite answer.

Do you think I'm trying to weave a spell? Perhaps so; we may need an incantation now and then to break free of the materialism and the disbelief that would strangle us.

My glimpse of eternity, my hint of peace, majesty, and power transcending life itself, is high in the Saguache mountains in Colorado. I saw it first as a boy and didn't fully realize what I saw. Now I treasure it as an old man. But the contact is more enduring than the span of a man's life. To stand before the face of God is to stand outside time itself.

How many men visited this valley? How many dreamers have the Colorado mountains seen? Every personality, every event, hangs in timeless suspension at this enchanted place. The very bowels of the earth were predestined to thrust mountains into the sky to frame the setting. The wind and water were commanded to mold the scene.

The Indian, the trapper, the miner, the homesteader, the railroad man, the rancher — all who have since come here to act out some part of their lives — have each relinquished a bit of life now caught in a timeless embrace. What we do before God cannot be easily forgotten; the echoes and shadows of those people and those actions are still with us.

For me, to stand in this valley is to touch the lives of all those who have preceded us in God's memory. They are all here. They speak when we listen. The stories they tell belong to this place. The idea has been growing on me for a long time that some of the stories about this place and people should be told while I can still do it. For the last few years I've been fitting some of those stories together.

Once I was the boy who visited this valley. The days were long but the years were short. Somewhere along the way I became a dreamer of dreams, watching men come and go. Now I'm the old man who sometime soon must himself go home again — home to the face of God.

The last three quarters of a century have gone by in a hell of a hurry, and there's a lot of it I probably didn't understand. But there's one thing I know for sure.

They say you can't go home again.

They're wrong.

II
CONVERSATION AT THE CABIN

By the second winter back in the Gulch, I was getting to be a real mountain goat, and reveling in it. Gibby Gregg often came up to the cabin to drink some whiskey and settle the problems of the world. I always enjoyed those visits.

Gibby usually came alone, but once he brought a friend, a newspaper reporter from Denver, Jack Forester. The afternoon the country editor and the big-city reporter decided to come for a visit was a late November day which had started clear enough, but early afternoon was already bringing snow flurries. Midafternoon brought a falling temperature and a steady, heavy, wet snow that warned of a real blizzard. By then Gibby and Forester were already on the way from Buena Vista. Gibby wasn't a man easily discouraged by the weather — or anything else — so they kept coming. The snowfall reached blinding dimensions as the Gulch grew dark even earlier than usual. I wasn't expecting company and had settled in for a snowbound evening. The wind had come up and was driving the snow against the windows in dull thuds. The fire in the grate crackled as the wind roared in the chimney. By then you couldn't see two feet in the snow and the dark.

Gibby and Forester had made it within a mile of the cabin when the snow-clogged windshield wipers on the jeep left them so blinded that they lost the road and slid down a hill sideways, landing broadside against a tree. Gibby and Forester were both dumped face down in the snow, a few feet farther down the steep hill. The trip back up the hill was a tough climb in the deepening snow and the blinding wind and darkness. Finding the road to the cabin, and then staying on it, was mostly an act of faith. A mile on foot at night in a blinding mountain storm is more than enough to raise doubts in a man's mind about whether or not he's going to make it.

Gibby ran into the old Dodge Power Wagon at last and knew he was almost at the cabin. I had strung a rope from the road to the cabin to give me a guide in the dark or in a storm. My first sign of company that night was the sight of Gibby and his *Rocky Mountain News* friend lurching through the door in a cloud of snow, looking for all the world like two giant snowmen.

I brought my guests to the fire and soon had them warm, dry, full of food, and half full of whiskey. Gibby told me the whole story of the trip up the Gulch. He'd obviously enjoyed it immensely. Forester had obviously not. He'd forgotten, if he ever knew, how scared a man could be in a mountain storm. You could see the difference looking at the two men: Gibby — big, ruddy, his own man; Forester — small, slightly soft, alternately self-important and self-pitying. Forester couldn't decide whether the climb to the cabin in that snowstorm had made him a hero or a victim.

It turned out that Forester's interest in coming up to see me in the first place was to do a story in the *News* on why a "highly successful New York mining tycoon" would choose to disappear into a tiny valley in the Rockies. He had graduated from the University of Colorado with Gibby and had maintained the connection over the years. It was from Gibby that he learned about me in the first place.

With the storm raging outside, no one was going anywhere for at least the night. Gibby settled in for some drinking and some talk. He couldn't wait to see what was going to happen between Forester and me. He didn't have long to wait.

Forester was full of "progress" and "planning." His gods were all located in the future. The past was a dead weight for Forester; the sooner we outgrew it, the better. He couldn't understand why I would leave the future, leave New York, leave the progress and planning, leave the movers and shakers. Why trade all that for this hole-in-the-wall cabin in the wilderness? Did I really think those backwater jerks in Buena Vista or in any other small town had any idea of the future? The world was getting too complicated for all that sentimental hogwash. The future belongs to the intellectuals, the planners, and the people who've outgrown the past.

I believe Forester had intended to find out what made me tick, but he was too full of resentment that such people still existed, that somebody who ought to know better rejected his future. He was into his lecture pitch in the first ten minutes.

I didn't give a damn what Forester thought. He was little more than a peculiarly graphic example of everything that didn't interest me. After listening for quite a while, and watching Gibby squirm with anticipation of what he thought was about to come, I finally spoke up.

"You say things are getting complicated. You're right, they are. There are too damn many plans and planners, too many rules, too much government. That's what makes things so complicated. My Grammaw used to say that the more complicated the plumbing, the easier to stop up the drain."

Forester bridled. "I've been hearing that drivel from the old mossbacks as long as I can remember. It's those old poops who feel that way who hold up progress."

"I suppose that depends on what you call progress. The people you call mossbacks and old poops never did any planning for 'society' or any other abstraction. They spent their time taking care of their friends and their families. Those tough old men and women, the real doers, didn't spend their time taking care of the world. They were too busy taking care of their loved ones. In the process people like that usually made a lot of mistakes, but their love was real. They were real people, not some damn abstract intellectual exercise. You see, Forester, the world's full of arrogant sons of bitches like you and me. There's only one important difference between us: you want to run my business. I don't want to run yours. I just want you to leave me and mine alone. Especially don't crowd the kids. Give 'em room to think up something new, something that you and I may be so resentful about that we haven't been able to see it for what it is. The kids will come up with a real future if you and the planners stay the hell out of the way."

Forester had nowhere to go. Gibby was loving every minute of it. Forester turned to him and said, "My God, Gibby, can you believe this man? Surely you have some ambition for your country!"

Gibby looked him right in the eye and announced, "I can be accused of a lot of things, my friend, but being ambitious isn't one of them — unless ambitious means wanting to take care of your friends, defend the things you believe, protect your family. Then I'm ambitious enough to do whatever needs to be done. People with self-important ambitions shouldn't get in the way of what I can do for my friends or family or values. That's the way the American people used to feel. And if they feel that way again, they'll take back their country and they'll show the whole world what life is all about."

When I look back on that snowbound night in the cabin, I think I may have been a little hard on Forester. He and people like him aren't bad people; they're just confused, out of touch with their roots. One of the saddest parts of the sixties and seventies was the gap that opened between average Americans and the new-class intellectual and professional people who presumed to speak for the rest of us. All that enlightenment and self-congratulatory abstract caring cut off the new class from its roots, values, and fellow citizens. Worse still, these confused "beautiful people" were running much of the country and screwing up things for the rest of us.

And how confused they've been! Compassionate, yet failing to see that compassion is always particular, never general. Concerned with healthy feelings, but unable to distinguish between mental health and sanity. Obsessed with intelligence, but unable to see that IQ is not a tool for measuring love. Frantically planning and measuring "society," but never understanding that such measurement is oriented to quantity, not quality — giving us the wrong tools to tell anything really important about people or ideas.

Gibby was right that night. Since our self-appointed leaders are so screwed up, the American people must do the job on their own, the way they did when things were working right. We'll just have to get on with earning our livings, raising our kids, worshipping our God, and valuing the same truths that have always been there at the center of our lives. When the American people have that kind of confidence in themselves, we'll then see some genuine progress!

It was that night that the first ideas for this little journal started taking shape. I haven't told Gibby or anyone else about it, but I've begun to think that everyday people, some of the mountain types I'd been around since I was a kid, have a story that someone ought to tell. I've known many of them — colorful, tough, loyal, part of another time and place that may yet return.

III

AN OLD WOMAN AND A BOY

Dinner was over. The chores were finished and the dishes were done. The mountains loomed high to the west, outlined by a summer twilight an hour past sunset. Tree frogs were coming awake in the cottonwoods along the Platte. I sat on the front steps of the small white frame house, looking out to the mountains, feeling the darkness grow around me. Twilight has always been my favorite time. On those summer evenings the mountains seemed even larger and nearer, so near that their great shadow was still present after the daylight was gone and night had come.

The screen door opened behind me. I knew without looking that my grandmother had come out to sit in her rocker. This was her house. My own home was several miles away in South Denver. In 1912, only a few houses were scattered along the Platte River south of Denver. There was a great deal of room for a boy to explore, and I was free to roam at will along the river bottom. In summer I spent more time with Grammaw Hagee than I spent at home. Late afternoons I could usually be found at my grandmother's feeding the chickens, cutting wood for the stove, and staying for dinner.

Grammaw Hagee and I understood each other. We could sit for hours and say nothing. Sometimes we'd talk, asking the questions that young boys ask, and giving the answers grandmothers give.

"Aren't the mountains a picture tonight? Gosh, Grammaw, I wish I could paint a picture that looked like those mountains *really* look. There's something about them that everybody ought to understand."

"George, artists write books and paint pictures because they feel just like you do. An artist wants others to understand something that he thinks is important."

"Grammaw, I'm no artist. It's just that sometimes when I watch those mountains I feel — I don't know what I feel. But I know it's important."

"You don't need to be an artist to feel that way. We all do. George, every person in this world tells how he feels, what's really important to him, every day of his life. Every day we live, we paint another picture, write another chapter in our book. When we live our lives, we tell the world what's important to us."

"What should be important in a person's life, Grammaw?"

"Different people have different answers to that question, George. Some answers are better than others, but there are lots of good answers. From time to time you'll find some good ones. The trick when you run across a good answer is to hold it tight. Don't let anybody talk you

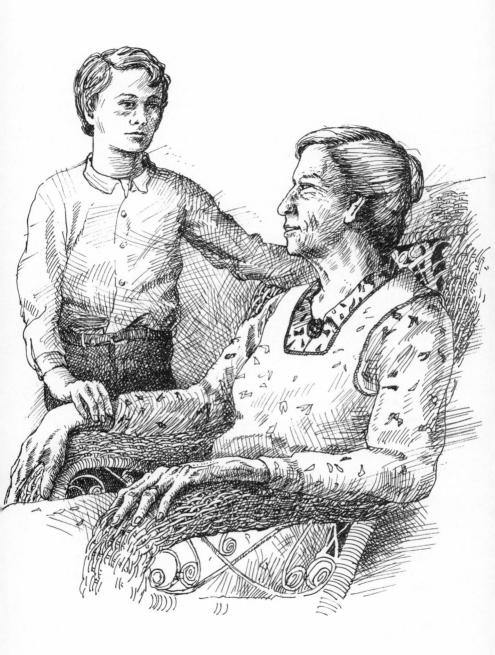

out of it. Remember, George, there are some things that shouldn't be forgotten."

Ellen Hagee had many things to remember. Perhaps that's why she was such a good grandmother for a young boy. She and her husband had come to Colorado from Texas, traveling in a covered wagon, homesteading the land and building the house in which she still lived. She had worked, and worked hard, in a life which offered more hardship than most.

Three years after homesteading their land along the Platte south of the small mining and cattle town of Denver, she had lost five of her six children in an epidemic of German measles.

Two years later, another child was born to the Hagees, two months premature, kept alive through a bitter winter in a basket next to a wood stove.

Five years later, Grampa Hagee died in a blizzard, trying to get home through drifts waist deep. No one ever knew for sure, but apparently he was crossing a railroad trestle over the Platte when, blinded by the swirling snow and the biting wind, he plunged to his death in the darkness.

Ellen Hagee kept her homestead, raised her daughters, and earned a living in downtown Denver where she toiled as a seamstress for nearly forty years. She daily trekked to and from downtown Denver — including the three-mile walk each way from the end of the streetcar line to her home. She raised the chickens and kept the garden, did the canning and sewing for herself and her girls, lived to see them happily married, and found the time to sit on the porch with her favorite grandson as the twilight deepened behind the mountains on a summer evening.

Yes, Grammaw Hagee had many things to remember. Her memories were likely to be direct and to the point. She was not one for self-pity and idle chatter. Tough and self-reliant, composed and determined, this fine old pioneer lady was not a very social person. But she had a soft spot in her heart for me. And it was at her tiny white house in the shadow of the mountains that I first heard some of those "answers" about life:

— "Find out who you are and never forget it, George."

— "Value yourself and your privacy."

— "Get some land with water, George, and hold it."

— "Put your trust in God. You'll still have to face the things you fear, but with God's help you'll discover there's nothing really to be afraid of."

Out of the pioneer spirit of an earlier time came those occasional comments, usually an accidental part of a longer conversation, and nearly always on that small front porch which looked up to the mountains. Land, water, privacy, a sense of identity with oneself and one's God — I was hearing the voice of the pioneering, westward-moving nineteenth century as I prepared to live in the brand new and very different twentieth century.

"Grammaw, what does God look like?"

"The face of God is always there, George, in the smile of a friend or a loved one. Sometimes you can see the face of God in a favorite place or a favorite time of day. You and I see the face of God when the sun goes down behind the mountains. I suppose the face of God is always there — so long as you're doing the right thing. The trick is to make sure that you *really are* doing the best you can. It doesn't make any difference how you fool other people. Sometimes the tiniest obligation is the one that only you — and God — know you have to fulfill. That's when you'll find the face of God."

"I've got to go home now, Grammaw."

"Good night, George."

A Sense of Space

Denver's new century was far different from its pioneer days, but most of the big changes were yet to come. In 1912 the easy pace and the open space were still there. Denver, like me, was still growing up in 1912. Youth is a confusing time, for a city, a boy, or any of us. The present moment's nice, but we can't stay there forever. We all must resume our long trip to an unknown destination. If we're honest, we will admit that we're anxious to be on our way, but how we hate to leave so much behind.

There was plenty to enjoy in the Denver of 1912 — always space, room to move. The great prairie stretched eastward hundreds of miles from the mountains and surrounded Denver. In 1912 the prairie not only surrounded the growing little Queen City of the Plains, but also covered whole city blocks within Denver proper. Milk cows were pastured across the street from the state capitol. The cottonwoods and cattails grew around the edge of many a prairie lake that would one day be landscaped residential property miles from the nearest open country. Overlooking all that open space, towering then and now in the imagination, were the mountains. A young boy and a young city had a sense of space. A great gift indeed.

A youngster also had a chance to see the living past. Buffalo Bill was a steady customer of the Denver hotels and saloons in 1912. His flowing white mane of hair and beard and his regal presence were living emblems of the pioneer past. The battle to the death with Yellow Hand was refought in the adoring eyes of every youngster who saw Buffalo Bill entering the Brown Palace Hotel.

In 1912, amusements abounded for the young wanderer. For the enormous sum of five cents (cash), I could ride throughout Denver aboard a streetcar. For an additional nickel, a traveler could take the "interurban car" to Golden, ten miles west to the first range of the foothills rising toward the Rockies.

Neighborhood saloons before Prohibition were filled with their own smells of hops and horseradish. The dark interiors glistened with the icy sweat of the glasses and the shine of the brass bar rail, dimly lighting the large oil painting of Venus which always hung behind the bar. Openhanded bartenders usually made it easy for a kid to pick up a free lunch and a glass of beer, in return for running a few errands delivering buckets of beer to neighborhood customers. While we were running those errands, the chance for a little creative graffiti was always available. Denver in 1912 still used arc lights. Stumps of carbon sticks discarded by the lamp tender made great crayons for scribbling on fences and sidewalks.

Practically everybody's favorite way to spend an afternoon was a visit to Elitch's Gardens. John Elitch, a Denver restaurant owner, built an amusement park in North Denver, with band concerts, summer theater and zoo. His big attraction was Ivy Baldwin, the famous balloon ascensionist, performing for sellout crowds Saturday and Sunday afternoons. Baldwin would swing on his trapeze suspended beneath the balloon, while soaring high above the city. The performances usually concluded with Ivy parachuting to safety, except when he ran into a tree and broke a few bones. Baldwin offered a five-dollar reward for the return of one of his balloons. Many a youngster spent Saturday afternoon among the cottonwoods on the South Platte, or the sagebrush on the prairie east of Denver, looking for one of those treasures, spending and respending in his imagination that princely five-dollar reward.

The Fourth of July in those days still brought the big celebrations it had in the pioneer West. The independence celebrated was a tangible commodity. The average citizen *was* largely free. People scarcely knew government existed. There were a mayor, a governor, a president, and the rest of elected officialdom, but the man in the street saw no real connection between his daily life and those distant dignitaries.

This sense of independence revealed itself in many ways. Winfield Scott Stratton, an illiterate ex-carpenter who discovered the vastly rich Independence Mine, was once refused by a desk clerk when he tried to register at the fashionable Brown Palace Hotel accompanied by a blonde lady of the evening. Stratton marched out of the lobby and crossed the street to the restaurant where the owner of the Brown was having dinner. Stratton bought the hotel on that spot for $800,000 cash, fired the desk clerk, and moved into the bridal suite with his blonde. The frontier was still alive in Denver.

For all its pioneer exuberance, a sense of stability and assurance marked Denver in 1912. The horse troughs were green and smooth, pork chops were fifteen cents a pound, and the butcher could be counted on to throw in a soup bone (and the vegetables to make the soup) for no charge with your grocery order. Life was generally a little quieter and slower. Memorial Day, the holiday which in 1912 Americans still knew as Decoration Day, was the special day for the GAR. The Grand Army of the Republic, veterans of the Civil War, turned out in force. The blue uniforms and the scent of lilacs mingled each spring. Civil War stories were told and retold, growing a little with each passing year. By 1912 the number of the old veterans was dwindling; each year a few more slept 'neath the sod. But new conflagrations of the new century were about to arrive, far larger and more impersonal than the Civil War.

Denver in 1912 gave us a feeling that we knew what the world was all about and where it was going. It was a good time and place to be ten years old.

Eight Chickens at Once

Certainly there was no shortage of things for a ten-year-old boy to do. Unfortunately, Emerson School interfered with my enjoyment of all those interesting things. Academic life was always a chore for me, an unpleasant but unavoidable fact of life.

Not that there weren't some bright spots along the academic road. All of us searchers after learning were delighted one fall when the algebra teacher at Emerson started losing his mind. Bit by bit during that Colorado autumn, the mental processes of this academic worthy became increasingly erratic. This Ichabod Crane of South Denver, with chalky fingers and complexion to match, gradually withdrew from reality until he would accept any solution to an algebra problem, the more bizarre and unworkable the better. We discovered this almost immediately and enjoyed several easy months before the school authorities caught on. Meanwhile we didn't learn any algebra, but we had a good time in a classroom where ridiculous algebraic solutions received the best grades. In fact, several competed to see who could achieve the greatest heights of absurdity when writing the problems on the blackboard.

Penmanship was another chronic difficulty for me. Before World War I, what used to be called Spencerian penmanship was still taught. Teachers periodically complained to my parents that I couldn't or wouldn't follow proper instructions, most especially that I failed to "use the forearm as a means of restful control." Grammaw Hagee told me that the Bible was full of stories about writing with moving fingers, but she'd never seen any biblical reference to writing with the forearm. I relayed the message to my teacher, who wasn't amused.

My schoolwork was usually the despair of my parents and teachers. But once in a while I did something right. One English teacher especially never lost faith in me. She selected me to enter a city-wide elocution contest, reciting Secretary of the Interior Lane's speech delivered at the dedication of the Panama Canal. I memorized and practiced for three weeks. At last the day of the contest dawned. With the speeches scheduled to begin at 6 P.M. in City Park Auditorium, I didn't have anything to do that Saturday except be dressed and ready in time to go with my parents to the contest.

Filled with grim forebodings about appearing before hundreds of people that evening, I looked up a few friends that Saturday morning to take my mind off impending doom. Billy Bonnie, Art Hammond, and a few more of us decided to go down to the car barns. That was our first mistake. The car barns in southwest Denver were the storage place for Denver's trolley cars. They were a great place to smoke cigarettes made with a mixture of tea and tobacco and rolled in brown wrapping paper. The car barns were also the no man's land where young toughs from South and West Denver were likely to confront one another. Those run-ins had produced lots of trouble before and somehow we always came back for more. In fact, there had been so many fights around the car barns that the policeman on the beat had warned all the would-be tough guys, "The next time there's trouble, I'll run the whole lot of you in!"

South Denver and West Denver peered at each other through a cloud of smoke. The policeman's warning was fresh in our minds. Nobody was looking for trouble. A few feeble tries at conversation failed for lack of a second, until a subject of universal interest came up: the preferred means of killing a chicken.

Some favored chopping off heads, others preferred

wringing necks. I topped all previous entries by announcing that my grandmother could put the neck of a chicken between each finger of each hand and wring all their necks at the same time. One West Denver kid pointed out the extreme unlikelihood of an old lady being able to wring the necks of eight chickens at one time. In fact, he went on to question Grammaw Hagee's integrity in making such a claim. I solved the dispute by slugging West Denver square in the mouth. Within about two seconds, everybody was in the fight. South Denver won by a narrow margin, following heavy casualties on both sides. Fights were not uncommon in Denver in the early years of the century, but this one was such a battle that the policeman who patrolled the car barns found it necessary to keep his promise. By 3 P.M. my father was called to the station house to get me out of jail. This turned out to be a real social occasion, because the parents of most of the brawlers were already acquainted. In fact, they'd met before in that very police station.

My father and I were home by 4 P.M., leaving just time enough to make the necessary repairs and dress for the big elocution contest. By the time my family reached the auditorium, where several hundred people were already gathered, my clothes were presentable, but it was obvious even from the audience that we couldn't do much to patch up a split lip and two black eyes.

I waited my turn on the platform with the inert faculties, the paralyzed nerves, and the fluttering heart experienced by generations of young speakers. When I finally mounted the podium, black eyes and all, my brain had turned to pudding. I couldn't remember a word of the speech.

As I stood there my glance came to rest on my mother and father, on the teacher who believed in me, and on Grammaw Hagee, whose face shone with such pride that I knew I couldn't let her down.

I caught fire and so did my speech. Secretary Lane's original dedication of the Canal was probably pale by comparison. On the way home afterward, the family rode toward Broadway on the westbound streetcar. The lights of Colfax Avenue, one of Denver's main streets, were bright at ten o'clock that Saturday night. Boasting two black eyes and a gold medal, I was oblivious to my surroundings as I sat on the wicker seat of the streetcar. My father asked once again who had started the fight. I told the whole story again, including the part about Grammaw Hagee's unique abilities as a chicken killer. Grammaw knew the family of the young man who doubted her neck-wringing skills: "I know the father and I know the son; when it comes to brains they could both switch theirs for a pie filling and nobody'd be any worse off but the pie."

My mother sniffed, "Now mother, that's no way to talk."

Grammaw Hagee smiled and gave me a hug. "Nonsense, that is *just* the way to talk. Never apologize for telling the truth, George."

Wilberforce J. Whiteman

I finally moved on from Emerson School and became a seeker after knowledge at South Denver High School. In those days, the director of vocal music for the Denver public schools was Wilberforce J. Whiteman, Paul's father. Wilberforce was a compact, dapper man, immaculately dressed and groomed in every detail, down to his waxed mustache. An accomplished violinist, organist, and choir director, he reigned over the Denver musical community for forty years.

On his weekly visits to the various schools in Denver, Whiteman sometimes needed more than his musical abilities. There were times when the manly art of self-defense was an absolute must. During his visits to the schools,

Whiteman would conduct impromptu auditions while an entire classroom was singing, stopping by the desks of students and listening to discover potential choir members. After listening to me one day, Whiteman paid me the only compliment I ever received for my musical ability, "George, you sing in a perfect monotone."

Some students didn't appreciate the frankness. More than once the dapper director of music found it necessary to defend himself on the school grounds after class. Once while visiting one of the schools, Whiteman urged a would-be bass to sing tenor, much to the amusement of the young tough's friends. One thing led to another and soon the word was circulating throughout school that the big kid was "waiting" for Whiteman outside. The principal advised the director of music to leave by a rear door, especially since the young man was a head taller and thirty pounds heavier than Whiteman.

What neither the principal nor the unfortunate young man knew was that Whiteman had been a credible middleweight boxer in his day. With the customary grace that he displayed in all his actions, Whiteman nonchalantly strolled out the front door. When the big kid loomed up before him, Whiteman set him up with a left hook and dumped him on his backside with a right cross. The respect that Whiteman enjoyed in Denver's tough neighborhoods as the result of those encounters gained for him a lasting reputation and an affection that continued through several generations of Denver kids, with no apparent harmful effects to their musical abilities or their psyches.

Uncle Phil

It was great to be a tough kid in a tough young country. The possibilities were limitless. My father's little brother Jake was just a few months older than I and lived in Leadville with my grampa. One Saturday when Uncle Jake was visiting us in Denver, he, Billy Bonnie, and I visited Brucie Gordon, a fellow sufferer at South Denver High. Brucie lived in a mansion complete with butler and maid. The Gordons were a little on the patrician side, at least in their own estimation, but Brucie could usually be counted on for a good time.

This particular Saturday we were pursuing scientific knowledge. Brucie's father had a large collection of wax recording cylinders featuring the stars of European opera. The collection was the pride of the Gordon household. Evenings brought guests from far and wide to hear "the finest in European operatic voices." This collection of wax recording cylinders was the object of our scientific experiment that Saturday morning. Inventors that we were, we decided to try an experiment, reheating the wax cylinders in the oven, then allowing them to reharden. Using the needle as a stylus, we shouted into the Victrola horn, hoping to record our voices. The experiment was a failure. We had succeeded only in converting Europe's finest operatic voices into a chorus of indistinguishable grunts.

These recording efforts were over by early afternoon. By then it was beginning to dawn on Brucie that his father might not be pleased with the results of our recording experiment. We were about to leave when Mr. Gordon entered the house. Home unexpectedly in an era when men still spent Saturdays at the office, Brucie's father brought two of his clients into the living room. Mr. Gordon was an exceedingly unwelcome sight for us just then. Addressing his friends, Mr. Gordon boomed, "Pour yourselves a drink and sit down. You're in for a treat. This is the finest collection of European operatic talent you'll ever hear!"

At that moment we decided that some fresh air might be welcome, but were interrupted midflight by Mr. Gordon's powerful voice: "Sit down, boys. I see you've been using the cylinders. Stay and hear more. I'm glad to see that you youngsters are beginning to appreciate the finer things!"

The only thing we would have appreciated at that moment was a speedy departure, but Mr. Gordon wouldn't take no for an answer. He was puzzled but pleased at Brucie's sudden interest in opera. The young recording scientists found themselves sweating with apprehension as the first cylinder was placed in the machine.

"Now we're really going to hear something!" said Mr. Gordon, settling back and beaming with satisfaction.

He heard something all right, something roughly analogous to a cross between an Indian snake chant and a Kentucky hog-calling contest. The results were electrifying. Mr. Gordon gaped in disbelief, then rushed to the machine to try another cylinder, then another.

Throughout all the excitement we sat with frozen faces and wildly beating hearts. As the fourth cylinder gave out with its weird grunts, Brucie, Billy, Jake, and I rose as one man, mumbling excuses while heading for the door.

"Wait just a damned minute!" Mr. Gordon was beginning to see our activities in an entirely new light. As it turned out, he evinced no appreciation for our scientific inquiry. Saturday night and all day Sunday were a time of troubles for Brucie in the Gordon home. Each of us expected to face similar hot water at our own homes after Mr. Gordon made his promised telephone call to our fathers.

Billy, Jake, and I each invested a nickel in a streetcar ride across Denver and another nickel for the interurban to Golden. We spent an apprehensive afternoon hanging around Golden and finally caught the last car back to Denver that night. It was late Saturday night when I finally faced the inevitable. I arrived home to discover that my parents were waiting up long past their accustomed bed-time. Saturday's search for scientific knowledge had a painful conclusion.

Fortunately, youth is irrepressible. A week later we four adventurers were looking for another challenge. This time we found it on a rail overpass south of Denver. One of our favorite locations for adventure was the rail yard and the tracks along the Platte River. One overpass in particular was a regular stop. We'd lie in wait, well armed with horse apples (of which Denver had a plentiful supply in those days), ready to ambush a train as it slowed for arrival in the Denver yards. In those days brakemen still rode the tops of cars because the brakes of each car had to be set by hand. The point of the game was to bombard the un-lucky brakeman with the horse apples and then duck out of sight behind the railing of the bridge which ran over the tracks. One nervous brakeman, perhaps thinking him-self assaulted by tramps pelting him with rocks, drew his revolver that Saturday afternoon and sprayed the bridge railing with several bullets. We looked at one another and decided that duty called elsewhere, for that Saturday and several Saturdays to come.

There were other occasions, though, when we enjoyed the last laugh, as we did one evening in Cherrylyn. That memorable evening began innocently enough. In Denver before World War I, it was always possible to spot a home where a party was planned. On the back porch would be a telltale wooden tub of ice cream, specially delivered for the occasion. Billy, Jake, Paul Whiteman, and I, spotting one that evening, decided to snitch it and throw a party of our own. Stealing the tub was easy, but we soon discov-ered we'd stolen a tub of butter by mistake. Rather than allow the butter to go to waste, we decided to take the tub to Cherrylyn.

Cherrylyn was the southernmost point of the streetcar

tracks in Denver. The old yellow cars with the narrow gauge and the great broad wooden bodies drew their power from a single trolley overhead. At the south end of the line, the streetcars ran out Broadway, turning east to climb a steep hill for several blocks — Lincoln, Sherman, Grant — then changed directions on a turntable, waited for five minutes, and headed west for several blocks back down the steep hill, turning north on Broadway and heading back to downtown Denver.

We waited until the last car of the night had climbed the hill at Cherrylyn. Then we used the butter to smear the tracks in the last block of the steep hill, between Lincoln and Broadway, withdrawing to the sidewalk to await results. We weren't disappointed — in fact, the spectacle almost exceeded our wildest expectations. The sleepy motorman came nodding down the first two blocks of the hill, riding the brakes all the way as usual. The streetcar wheels reached the greased portion of track and the car slid the entire last block, nearly careening off the rails as it turned on Broadway. By then the motorman was fully awake.

There was no shortage of mischief to discover. There also was no shortage of jobs, and most of us began to hold down a part-time job or two quite early. I'd been cutting grass and delivering beer for years. By the time I was twelve I had a regular job after school for the Gates Rubber Company delivering truck tires, which I carried over the handlebars of my bike. I was delivering one of those tires out south Broadway late one afternoon after school when I rode too close behind a skittish horse.

I was kicked in the chest and face. Receiving word at home, my parents rushed to the hospital, arriving in the growing dark of a winter evening. As they told me later, the grim doctor warned them that it would be a miracle if I lived. The first of several such miracles occurred and

I lived. Still have the imprint of a horseshoe on my collarbone.

My next job was with the Denver Tramway Corporation. When applying for the job, I didn't mention my previous tramway experience at Cherrylyn. I was thirteen now and hired on as a conductor, the number two man who collected fares while the motorman ran the streetcar. The conductor was number two in every respect but one: the Denver Tramway had an inviolable rule that the motorman, located in the front of the streetcar, could *not*, under any circumstances, start the streetcar until the conductor, located in the rear of the streetcar, had rung the bell. This rule eventually cost me the job.

It had to happen sooner or later. The streetcar on which I was conductor was just turning onto Broadway at the south end of the line. The car stopped to take on passengers. It was at this southernmost stop that Grammaw Hagee daily concluded the three-mile walk from her house and caught the streetcar to her seamstress work in downtown Denver. The old lady was a fast walker in spite of her bad hip, but she was still almost two blocks from the streetcar stop when I saw her coming. I began to wait and the motorman began to fume. The waiting and fuming continued until the motorman marched back to the rear of the car. "When you going to ring that bell, kid?"

"When my grandmother gets here."

"I don't give a damn about your grandmother, kid. Now ring that bell."

"I don't give a damn about you. I'll ring the bell when I'm good and ready!"

Grammaw Hagee caught the streetcar and I lost my job.

There were other jobs coming. I was fourteen now and big for my age. This presented some new job possibilities, especially when I accompanied Uncle Phil on his rounds as a salesman for a produce wholesaler. Uncle Phil was a large, easygoing man with broad shoulders and gigantic paws for hands. He was pleasant and talkative as any sales-man, but was the kind who was willing and able to defend himself when the need arose, as it often did in the tough wholesale produce business of Larimer Street.

Uncle Phil was in and out of the saloons and restaurants on Larimer Street, a regular drinking partner of his many business associates. Sometimes I went with him on his rounds, and had long since mastered the art of maintaining a standing position on the brass rail without holding on. When I'd been smaller this left both hands free, one for pretzels, the other for beer.

Uncle Phil liked to have me along. Sometimes this made him a little careless about inquiring whether school was in session that particular day. This angered the authorities, but it always pleased me. On those trips, Uncle Phil would usually grow more and more expansive as the day's drink-ing wore on. As he made his way from one stop to the next, sometimes he could even be urged to talk about the old days when Indians still roamed the plains. It was always easy to tell how much Uncle Phil had been drinking, be-cause at a certain stage of advanced inebriation he always began telling the same story. He'd describe his trip west as a young man, walking behind a covered wagon from Illinois to Colorado. On that trip he had one day left the wagon train for a moment of personal business, when he was set upon by Indians. He escaped with his life, but incurred a wound that marked him forever. Should any doubting Thomas question the existence of such a wound, Uncle Phil would drop his pants to display the facts of the matter, adding, "If I still had them old pants, I could prove there was no arrow hole in them, neither!"

Travels with Uncle Phil were never dull. Once on the way home after one of those afternoons, Uncle Phil and I noticed the dog of a neighbor, locked in a dogcatcher's wagon with twenty other unfortunate mutts. Uncle Phil explained that he knew the dog and requested his release. The dogcatcher was unmoved and surly, suggesting to the world at large that kids and drunks shouldn't harass public officials who were doing their duty.

Uncle Phil surveyed the situation, spied a crowbar leaning against the woodshed of a nearby house, and went into action. It was the work of an instant to grasp the bar, march to the wagon, and smash the padlock. A moment later, twenty dogs raced to freedom as an enraged dogcatcher, returning to the scene, witnessed his day's work completely undone.

"What do you think you're doin'?" screamed the public servant. "You can't do that!"

"I already done it," replied Uncle Phil, who stood leaning on his crowbar with a look that invited further discussion of the subject. Eyeing Uncle Phil, the dogcatcher departed, leaving Uncle Phil and me in an expansive mood as we headed home. Throwing his arm around my shoulder, Uncle Phil advised, "Never let 'em push you around, George!"

My next job came through the good offices of Uncle Phil. I was offered a chance to drive a delivery wagon for a butchershop on South Logan. I took the job without the slightest knowledge of how to run one of the new horseless carriages. I had admired the new speeding contraptions from afar, but had never set foot in one. The first day on the job found me struggling with the crank, unable to start the monster. A sympathetic butcher came out and showed me how to choke the Ford and advance the spark before I turned the crank. The delivery wagon started, I climbed behind the wheel, depressed the clutch pedal of the Model T, and was off in a blaze of glory. From that day to this, I never got over my love affair with the automobile.

Grammaw Hagee never exactly approved of Uncle Phil's

drinking, and she was always sure to notice when I had drunk a beer or two. But if she had something to say, she usually managed to say it privately. Early in the spring of my fourteenth year, with the wind sweeping off the mountains and freezing the winter-shrunk bed of the South Platte, I dropped off some oxtails and a pork loin at Grammaw Hagee's small house. Actually, the route for my meat deliveries didn't run so far south of town, but I usually found a way to stop by and visit Grammaw Hagee.

Grammaw promptly detected the beer on my breath that day, commenting to no one in particular, "The more sure a man is that he can handle alcohol, the bigger fool he is. Remember that, George."

"Yes, Grammaw."

The harsh winds of late winter and early spring were giving way to the balmy days of a Rocky Mountain thaw. Springtime had come to the Rockies again. I was now fifteen. Denver and I were growing up, and neither of us knew how big the changes were which lay just ahead.

Things That Won't Come Again

It was in the early spring of 1917 that an attorney first contacted the family to clear the title of a mining property located in the mountains above Idaho Springs. Grammaw Hagee dug the papers from her husband's carefully stored effects. It appeared that the family did have a small, long-standing claim based on a few dollars Grampa Hagee had invested years before. Grammaw Hagee determined to go to the claim herself.

My grandfather Walter Stewart was a mining engineer working in Leadville and it seemed like a good idea to ask him to help us. I don't really know why she didn't. Two reasons, I guess: Grammaw Hagee never asked anybody's help for anything; and Grammaw Hagee and Grampa

Stewart never got along — too much alike, I suppose. When I made the mistake of bringing it up, Grammaw said, "Why ask Grampa Stewart? He'd be no help. I don't speak ill of the dead, and that's what he'll be if he keeps drinking."

When she determined to do something, Grammaw Hagee *did* it. She packed her bag, collected me, and set out for Union Station to catch a train west and south into the mountains, where she and I would be met in Idaho Springs by the attorney who would take us up the canyon to the claim.

The trip to Idaho Springs wasn't long, not even in 1917. But it was an exciting adventure for a young boy: westward out of Denver, reaching Golden, and then heading up Clear Creek Canyon, with the sun glinting on the brasswork of the old steam engine. Cattle grazing in occasional clusters raised their heads to watch the train go by. Hereford calves stopped their play long enough to take a drink from the creek. An occasional cowboy stopped to roll a cigarette and wave as the train puffed past. The air was warm, the sun was bright, the mountains were fresh and clean as a Colorado spring.

After the hawker selling picture postcards and "genuine smoked glasses" to the train passengers had approached her three times, Grammaw Hagee, politely refusing each time, finally announced to the world in general, "Young man, I'm quite capable of looking out the window to see God's handiwork, and need no cheap postcard imitations."

Later she turned to me and murmured, "I should never have lost my temper with that man. Remember, George, when you lose your temper, you're always the real loser."

Our arrival in the small mining town of Idaho Springs was just the beginning of that day. The wagon ride up the mountain to the mine still lay ahead. The tall, angular lawyer who met us was a real frontier barrister. His black frock coat, dusty boots, and florid, leathery face could have been found in any mountain town. Half gone in drink when we started, he lost ground steadily for the balance of the trip. As we wound higher and higher into the mountains behind Idaho Springs, on a trail scarcely wide enough for the wagon, the attorney periodically nipped from the jug he carried in the floorboards. After some half-dozen pauses for refreshment, the lawyer dozed more and more, waking only when it was time for another drink.

Meanwhile, the mule plodded on without direction, completely oblivious to the precipice which lay at the edge of the winding, rocky trail. Grammaw Hagee finally turned to the lawyer and fixed him with a look that would freeze boiling water. "The Indians weren't any great shakes, Mr. McAllister, but at least when they were running things around here they used to wear their feathers outside their skulls — which is more than I can say for you. I'll take the reins now, *if you don't mind*."

The lawyer didn't mind a bit. He handed the reins to Grammaw, climbed into the back of the wagon, and promptly fell asleep. The undaunted Grammaw Hagee handed the reins to me. I'd driven a mule and wagon before, but never on such a trail. Grammaw Hagee looked straight ahead without comment for the balance of the trip, but I couldn't take my eyes off the precipice yawning next to the wagon. I could look into the tops of the pine trees below. Fortunately, the trail led straight to the mine with no other turnoffs. We found our way up the mountain and safely arrived at the mine.

A Colorado mining claim before World War I was a primitive and potentially dangerous place. The two old sourdoughs working the small claim were surprised to see a woman in their midst, but they were anxious to please and welcomed their guests warmly. Grammaw Hagee was on her best behavior and the tour of the operation was soon under way, including a trip far back into the tunnel that penetrated the hillside. I was astonished at her knowledge of such things. She seemed to have an eye for detail and an understanding of what the two old miners were attempting in their shoestring operation. Somehow I could imagine Grammaw Hagee living in such a remote mountain clearing, working long days in a tough, simple environment. Perhaps it was just in my eye, but the old lady seemed to take on the texture of the high mountain camp, becoming a part of the rocks and trees around her.

Grammaw Hagee seemed to enjoy the tour in the bright sunlight of the Colorado high country, and the sourdoughs enjoyed her. Finally we were through and the older of the two men diffidently produced a jug of whiskey and a tin cup from the cabin. The old lady politely declined and glanced at me in such an unmistakable manner that I also declined. The time had come to return to Idaho Springs and catch the train to Denver. The lawyer had even sobered up to the point of being able to pilot the wagon back down the mountain to the train station.

The rest of the family never understood why Grammaw wanted to visit the mine that day. The arrangements were already made to sell the family interest. There never was any large amount of money involved in settling the family claim to the property. But I knew why she wanted to go. On the way back down Clear Creek Canyon, with the last rays of the setting sun still lighting the peaks above us, I asked, "Grammaw, what do you think about when you look off in the distance and don't talk?"

"Old people look off in the distance to remember things which won't come again."

"I don't understand, Grammaw."

"One day you will, George."

Making the World Safe

Springtime in the Rockies is a special experience. The winter snows still hold the high country, but the chill winds sweeping across the foothills gradually soften to gentle breezes, bringing a freshness all their own. Spring fever has always afflicted the whole world, but nowhere is that malady more certain to strike than in clear, sweet mountain air. I'm afraid I was no exception as a kid.

On a May day in 1917 Billy Bonnie and I, both at Denver's South High School, were feeling the full effects of springtime in the Rockies. We decided that any more classes were out of the question for the day, so we adjourned to nearby Washington Park. The sun was warm, the grass was green, the air was heavy with the scent of spring flowers. We were ready for a call to high adventure, leading in almost any direction except back to school.

Lying on my back and watching the clouds drift through a deep blue sky, I told Billy that the navy was taking all comers. "It'd surprise everybody if we enlisted in the navy!"

"George, your folks wouldn't ever let you do it. My dad would kill me. Besides, you're fifteen and I'm sixteen — the navy's not taking 'em that young."

Should we join the U.S. Navy and see the world, or should we go back to Mrs. Weber's English class? The more we talked, the better the navy sounded: returning to Denver as heroes in naval uniforms — applauded by our classmates and teachers, the envy of everyone.

Something besides spring fever was working that warm May 1917 afternoon. America had just decided to make the world safe for democracy. The atrocities of the Huns and the high ideals of the Allies were on the pages of every newspaper. In fact, the national director of the propaganda effort for the Wilson administration was a Denver newspaperman, George Creel. Liberty Bond drives turned out big crowds to cheer street-corner orators speaking from flag-draped stands in downtown Denver. The *Denver Post* reported war news in screaming headlines printed three inches high in red ink. Young men lined up at recruiting offices featuring posters of a stern Uncle Sam who told each young man, "I want you!"

Two evenings after that afternoon in Washington Park, I was sitting in the late evening twilight with Grammaw Hagee. As usual, the old lady had little enthusiasm for the current excitement: "Too much ballyhoo is a sure sign that something crooked is going on. When everybody stands up to cheer, put your hand on your wallet!"

"Grammaw, that's just what the German-American paper says. They say we shouldn't be in the war."

Grammaw Hagee's patriotic ire was aroused: "When those idiots criticize our country, they show themselves as traitors or fools. Remember, George, this country isn't perfect, but it's the best opportunity for free men and women that the world ever had. Don't ever let anybody tell you otherwise."

"But, Grammaw, you're German — Hagee's a German name."

"Hagee's an American name now, and don't you forget it, young man!"

Three afternoons later two very nervous young men were waiting in line at a naval recruiting station in downtown Denver. I had grown into a stocky kid who easily passed for the seventeen years which I claimed in my interview with the chief petty officer. In an atmosphere less crowded and rushed, the chief might have caught the deception. But in 1917 the naval enlistment procedures were fairly lax. Both of us soon found ourselves standing in another line, this time for a physical. I passed with flying colors. Billy was color-blind.

As I finished dressing, I was handed more papers by the chief. "Take these home and get your folks to sign. You need their permission until you're eighteen."

The street lights were coming on as we caught a streetcar outside the recruiting office. We rode through downtown Denver, watching the evening lights as the car reached Broadway and turned south. The ride gave some time to think, and I started to get worried. It was beginning to register that Billy would *not* be coming with me. Somehow that seemed very different from going off to high adventure with a good friend. Then there was the additional problem of parental consent. It was one thing to stretch one's age a bit. It was quite another thing to ask your parents to ratify the lie, especially when they knew nothing about the enlistment. The night seemed even darker than usual as I dropped off the streetcar and walked the last few blocks home.

In those days, color-blindness tests were conducted using lengths of yarn in different colors. Billy arranged to retake the test. Late the night before the second test, we went over the colors again and again, attempting to teach Billy the colors according to the differing lengths of yarn. The experiment failed and Billy was rejected a second time. I now seemed certain to be on my way alone to naval training in San Diego. Last-minute efforts grew more desperate. I spent one whole evening in an unsuccessful effort to flatten my arches by jumping from the roof of a shed behind Billy's house. Things finally got so bad that I thought it was time to tell my parents about the enlistment.

Telling my parents was especially difficult. Both my mother and father worked. I loved my parents as much as any other kid, but I'd been largely on my own since I was ten years old. Perhaps that was one reason that the connection had always been so much closer between Grammaw Hagee and me.

My father was a stubborn Irishman who worked for the post office. He met and married Grammaw Hagee's older daughter when he was less than twenty and she only sixteen. Married right out of high school, my parents had worked and saved for their entire lives to own their own home. The road hadn't been easy. My mother worked in the china department of "Denver's finest store," Daniels and Fishers. As a young couple making their plans for the future, they decided that easy street would have arrived when the main salary from the post office reached the astronomical sum of ten dollars a week. They had long since reached and passed that point.

By 1917 the family had a home and possessions to match. They loved each other and they loved me. But there was no doubt that I had largely been making my own decisions for several years past. I earned my own money with a series of part-time jobs, coming and going as I pleased.

The night that I broke the news of my enlistment, the lights in the Roche household burned late. Somehow the enlistment made a great difference. My mother suddenly realized that her little boy was no longer so little. "I'll refuse to sign! Wait until those recruiters find out you're fifteen years old."

My father was more practical, "Now, Dess, give the boy a chance. The way things are going, he's nearly failed school this spring and he may not go back this fall. Military service might be good for him. After all, the navy isn't dangerous like the army."

"Oh, how can you say such things!"

"Dess, don't interfere. Lots of young men are enlisting. If I were a little younger, I'd go myself. Hell, the boy is almost sixteen."

It was Grammaw Hagee who settled things for me and my parents the next day. "George, did you take on an obligation to join the navy?"

"Yes, Grammaw."

"Then honor your obligation."

Finally my mother gave tearful acquiescence. I was "in the navy now." I was slated for an early July departure for San Diego. Somehow in those last days home, mountains, friends and family took on special meanings. My mother was resigned to the enlistment. My father seemed relieved that the problems of school were now finished once and for all.

The last night in Denver found the recruit visiting his grandmother in that small white house by the Platte which he had visited so many times.

"Gosh, Grammaw. I want to go and I know I'm man enough to do the job, but sometimes I think dad is glad to see me go. At least mom says she's sorry I'm going."

"George, give your father a chance. Women handle their feelings in a different way. It's all right for your mother to weep and carry on. Your father wouldn't be a man if he let you know how he feels. Besides, your father has confidence in you. He knows that no matter where you go or what happens, you're a man now and he doesn't have to worry about you anymore."

As we sat in the dusk and looked off toward the mountains, I thought, maybe that means I've grown up now.

As the tears welled in my eyes, I turned to hide my face from Grammaw Hagee and thought, well, if this is how it feels to be a man, then I don't like it!

Grammaw Hagee hadn't moved a muscle, but, as usual, she knew just what was on my mind. "You can't change how you feel, George, but you can remember one thing. Wherever you go and whatever you do, God is always with you."

As I walked home that night, God seemed especially close. The night was warm and the sky was perfectly clear. The shadow of the mountains loomed to the west. The stars burned with the special fire reserved for clear nights in the mountains. I could still hear my grandmother's voice, "Wherever you go and whatever you do, remember that God is always with you."

Grammaw Hagee and my folks saw me off from Union Station. Most of the passengers on the train were military personnel, men in uniform changing duty stations or young recruits in civilian clothes on their way to boot camp. As the train waited to pull out that morning, goodbyes were being said up and down the tracks. I clutched my tickets and my suitcase. I kissed and hugged both parents, but the last hug was for Grammaw Hagee. She whispered in my ear, "Remember who you are, George."

As the train headed west into the mountains, the young man found the rhythm of the wheels telling him again and again, "Remember who you are, remember who you are, remember who you are." As usual with Grammaw Hagee's cryptic remarks, I wasn't entirely sure what she meant, but I was sure it was important.

The train ride across a third of a continent was an adventure. I even found several recruits who were also on their way to navy boot camp in San Diego. Each youngster was as superficially cocksure and as basically unsure of what lay ahead as I was. Mostly I watched the big western country go by the windows of the train: mountains, desert, more desert and mountains, finally the orange groves of Southern California. I had, like all Americans of my generation, the impression that my nation was gigantic. But on my first long trip I began to realize just how large the country really was.

I changed trains on a hot, sticky afternoon in Los Angeles. By the time we reached San Diego I had spent forty-eight hours on the train. I thought I would be glad to depart the train, but I had no idea how wrong I was.

The cocky little boatswain's mate who met the recruits

as they left the train in San Diego knew how to handle boots. He launched immediately into the psychological warfare that lies at the heart of all boot training. I made the mistake of murmuring to the recruit next to me, "Who does that little bastard think he is?"

The boatswain's mate heard me. Thrusting his face upward into mine, he shouted, "When we get to base, you'll find out who I am, Junior!"

My education began that very day. Our platoon of recruits was standing at attention on the edge of a deserted parade ground, sweltering in the midst of a San Diego summer with our suitcases still at our sides. I found myself called out of the ranks, while the same squat drill instructor vented his spleen on "Junior."

"Junior thinks he's tough, don't you, Junior? Well, men, the navy is fair. The navy is going to give Junior a chance to show us just how tough he really is."

The navy of 1917 had several informal but binding customs, especially in boot camp, and the drill instructor was ready to play enforcer. The boatswain's mate stood on a small hump of ground with his hands on his hips, obviously waiting for me to come at him. In a moment, a ring of onlookers surrounded us. I had to put up or shut up. I had already decided I was an authentic tough guy, more than equal to navy boot camp, but was about to learn how wrong I was. Far larger than the agile little boatswain's mate, I discovered that I needed more than size to finish what I had started. The mate held the high ground in the center of the circle. Again and again I rushed that small mound, discovering that I couldn't dislodge the smaller man. I took a fearful beating in the process, but learned something that day: tough guys come in different shapes and sizes. I also learned not to charge with my head down.

As I stood there with a heaving chest, a split lip and a badly battered face, the mate asked if I was licked. Drawing on one of those conversations with Grammaw Hagee, I gasped, "I feel like Lazarus."

The mate's biblical training had been fairly limited. "Like Lazarus? What the hell are you talkin' about, Junior?"

"According to the Bible, Lazarus was licked by dogs."

That crack earned me a second beating. Another surprised recruit who was so unfortunate as to have been heard to snicker found himself knocked flat on the ground.

I survived boot camp, emerging bloody but unbowed. Something from out of the past, perhaps something from Grammaw Hagee, always stood me in good stead. Within weeks I was on the battleship *Virginia* heading through the Panama Canal, on my way to New York to load troops for the long crossing to France. The doughboys were on their way. I was assigned to kitchen duty on those crossings. Being a cook on a ship with a normal complement of eight hundred officers and men plus a troop contingent of three thousand men provided an opportunity to learn fry cookery on a wholesale basis. Frying ten thousand eggs for breakfast was a new experience.

Time passed fast, with too much work to get homesick. Sometimes on night watch, as the great ship moved through the silence, I'd notice the stars overhead, the same stars as in the mountains, yet somehow much more remote. It was going to be good to be back in the mountains again, where the stars burned at night just beyond a young man's fingertips.

"Wherever you go and whatever you do, remember that God is always with you."

The only real shooting action I saw was an incident in the mid-Atlantic when our gun crew sank a German submarine. We received a medal for the sinking, but I never saw the submarine at any time during the entire action. After that I wasn't so sure that all this hero business was quite so grand as advertised.

Trips to port were a lot more exciting. Trouble was, seamen first class didn't get to see much of Europe during 1917–18. In port only long enough to discharge troops and bring aboard stores, the USS *Virginia* was usually on the way back to New York with no shore leave for the crew. I did get liberty twice, both times in Marseilles. I saw enough to make me glad that my family was safe at home, well housed and well fed. Somehow I never got used to ten-year-old French boys trying to sell their older sisters to passing American sailors for a package of cigarettes. I'll never forget the utter weariness and decay Europe radiated. I went home convinced that the USA and especially the Rocky Mountains were really God's country, blessed beyond all understanding. Two twenty-four-hour passes in wartime Marseilles are probably insufficient for making such judgments, but I was so impressed with that idea that it has stayed with me for the rest of my life.

The false armistice came while I was ashore in New York. The town was delirious with excitement. It was a tickertape parade, the Fourth of July and St. Patrick's Day all rolled into one for the big town. The young seaman from Colorado watched a drunken marine sergeant, standing at the grill of a Child's restaurant on Lexington Avenue, cooking pancakes on one side and then flipping them upward to stick the uncooked sides against the ceiling. The sergeant was so drunk that he was leaning heavily against the wall for support, but he was having a wonderful time. Neither the regular cook nor anyone else in the crowded place seemed to mind. The war was over and it was time to celebrate.

As for me, I was a veteran of eighteen months. I'd learned not to charge with my head down. In fact, the big kid was fast becoming a man. It had been a long time now since I'd lost a fight. With my seventeenth birthday only a few months away, I looked twenty-three. I was as ready as anybody in New York that night to celebrate the end of the war, or at least thought I was.

The next morning I was on the Lower East Side, asleep beneath a hotel piano. Have you ever awakened with a bad hangover and your head beneath the sounding board of a grand piano while someone played "God Bless America" with the loud pedal down? My mouth was cotton, my head cement, and my pockets empty. As I hit the street, the newsboys were already shouting that the war wasn't actually over. The famous false armistice had come and gone. It was a sadder but wiser young man who came back to the USS *Virginia* that day.

The actual armistice soon came, but with no real change for the crew of the *Virginia*. The war ended, but the balance of 1918 and the first months of 1919 found the battleship still hauling troops, this time in the opposite direction. It was "over, over there," but another liberty in Marseilles made it clear to me that the Allied victors hadn't won much. The ten-year-old boys with sad eyes still offered their sisters for sale on the streets. I decided that night, the night of my seventeenth birthday, that the Great War, as nearly as I could tell, had only losers.

June 1919 saw me coming home, tougher and wiser as a seaman first class, a veteran of the Great War. On the train to Chicago, I rode westward with a shipmate, Ed Wall. It was great to be young and alive and heading home. In the club car on the way west from New York, we two sports were having the time of our lives. The war was over, we were going home, and our pockets were full of mustering-out pay.

"George, you've got to stay in Chicago with me for a few days. I know some great places — and wait till you see the girls we can get."

The closer the train came to Chicago, the better the whole idea sounded. The first night in town my wealthy ex-shipmate and I roared down Lake Shore Drive in a Pierce Arrow, by far the fanciest automobile this young Colorado kid had ever seen. As we reached 80 mph on that wild ride, I announced to Ed and the world, "I'm going to have a car like this — and soon."

Ed and I had been drinking too much to stay out of trouble. The 80-mph tour of Lake Shore Drive was the last straw. Half an hour later, we were standing before a police sergeant while he decided whether we were going to jail. Ed and I were both too far gone in drink to be discreet. Ed kept asking belligerently why it took two policemen to make an arrest. The third time Ed asked, I told him, "One cop can write, the other one can read."

We collapsed with laughter at this penetrating insight. The police sergeant was less amused and it was nearly noon the next day before Ed's family managed to get us out of jail.

The few days grew to a few weeks in Chicago. Ed was a good host. Besides, the youngster from Colorado was an entertaining diversion to the wealthy and bored young Chicago set Ed ran with. I had a few rough edges that were a real novelty to my newfound friends. When it came to raising hell, I was good company. When trouble was on the way, as it usually was in a Chicago roadhouse, I could be counted on to hold up my end.

The roadhouses around Chicago hosted Ed's Pierce Arrow during those June evenings in 1919. We made the rounds and I was usually in the company of one particular girl. Irene was blonde, good-looking, rich, and out for a good time. I was big, tough, bright, and (as usual) passing for an older and more experienced man. The combination produced results. June became July.

Ed Wall warned me, "Irene is a little snot. She's a good-looking snot, but she's still a snot. I like you, George; stay as long as you want. But don't get hurt."

"What do you mean?"

"I mean that you're bound to get hurt playing around with spoiled brats like Irene. She's got money; you don't. She's tennis and Marshall Fields and all kinds of things you're not."

Young and confident, I soon forgot what Ed said. But he was right and a storm was building.

It all ended one evening in a roadhouse across the Wisconsin line. I suppose the clash was inevitable. I was tired of raising hell, out of money, out of patience with Chicago, out of patience with myself. Irene was beginning to notice the change and thought, as "fast" young girls are likely to think, that I must have found someone more exciting. The roadhouse rang with a knock-down, drag-out argument.

Irene shouted some choice comments about "hicks from the mountains" and the crowd at the bar enjoyed it immensely. I threw one of them over the bar, bringing down the mirror and half the bottles on the shelves. Ed got me into the car and safely away before the police arrived.

The navy buddies closed several bars that night. By dawn I'd decided to go home. The mustering-out pay was long gone, but I still had my ticket to Colorado. In the early light of a summer morning in Chicago, Ed drove the Pierce Arrow through the deserted streets to LaSalle Street Station.

"I'll be back, Ed — in a Pierce Arrow."

"Yes, George, I believe you will."

"Take care, partner."

With aching head, I was on my way to Denver. For some reason of pride, I at the last moment refused the double eagle Ed pressed in my hand. On the train west that day and night, several times I wished I had been less proud. I was hungry. But even more, I was hurt. I was determined to make a success, to find that money just around the corner, to show the Irenes of this world they had less to be snotty about than they thought.

Early the next morning, as the train approached Denver, the hunger and the hurt passed away. Leaning far out from the platform between the cars, I caught my first glimpse of the mountains, ascending from the plains like a distant mirage. I realized more strongly than at any moment in the two years I'd been gone just how much I missed those mountains. I was coming home again.

I arrived in Union Station with nothing to eat for the twenty hours just past, but I knew where breakfast could be located. I went straight to the downtown shop where Grammaw Hagee worked as a seamstress.

We visited a small restaurant around the corner. She took my arrival as a matter of course, including the lack of money. "A fool and his money are soon parted, George," but the old eyes had a twinkle in them as she watched me eat a second plate of ham and eggs.

It was good to be home again, to see family and friends. But the best time was still at twilight, on the porch of my grandmother's house. I'd forgotten how good the sagebrush along the Platte smelled after a rain. I'd forgotten the beauty and peace of the mountains in a late summer twilight.

Grammaw Hagee and I talked late that night. The big goal at the moment was to earn plenty of money, enough money to get a car like that Pierce Arrow. I'd gone to war thinking I was tough. I'd come home convinced I was tough *and smart*.

Grammaw Hagee wasn't so sure. "You want to be careful what goal you pick, George — someday you might reach it. We all have to decide where we're going. If you make the right decision, you can't go wrong. If you know *why* you're living, you can always handle the *how*."

IV

LEADVILLE

When I was a kid, a giant bronze figure stood atop the Mining Exchange Building. He dominated downtown Denver. The old sourdough was dressed in the roughest work clothes and held a big nugget in his outstretched hand. He was, it seemed to me, the absolute soul of the nineteenth-century West, reaching out to the future — almost touching a vision of better times just around the corner. For me, that miner was my Grampa Stewart.

Walter Black Stewart was born in Scotland in the 1860s. He came to Canada to get an education and seek his fortune. Grampa Stewart chose McGill University where he entered medical school. Fate apparently didn't want him to be a doctor. He and his entire graduating class were expelled a few weeks before what was supposed to be their commencement. Considering the macabre sense of humor among medical students even at their best, I know that whatever my grandfather's class did must have been a

dandy. We'll never know for sure, because he would tell the story only that far — no further.

As a young man with medical training but no medical degree, Grampa Stewart decided to use some of his math background in mining. He headed for the goldfields in Colorado. In an era before a man had to have a license to earn a living, Grampa began his new career as a "mining engineer." Before he was through he lived through (and helped produce) a big piece of mining history.

In Colorado the "mining engineer" settled in Leadville and plunged into a new life with his typical optimism. Within a year he married an Irishman's widow, a few years older than he. That's quite a piece of optimism in itself. In the process he became my father's stepfather. By the time I first knew him, Grampa's wife was dead. His three stepsons had gone separate ways. My dad and Uncle Phil came to Denver. Uncle Jake was only a little older than I. He stayed in Leadville and grew up with Grampa Stewart. Grampa's home in Leadville gave him a base of operations to be a mining man and an old character with opinions on every subject. Uncle Jake and I spent a lot of time listening to those opinions while we were growing up. On the whole, a fairly tangled family trail, which Grampa Stewart never helped simplify in any way.

He wasn't close to the Roches or to Grammaw Hagee. They all looked on him with lifelong suspicion — which was probably justified. He warmly reciprocated that suspicion and was fond of getting together with the assembled descendants of his Irish Catholic stepfamily and addressing no one in particular with remarks like, "What a shame that a gentle and noble race like the Scot should be mingled with the Irish. I suppose God had His reasons. Certainly the Irish need all the civilizing influence they can get!"

He didn't limit his opinions to assaults on the Irish. In fact, Grampa was more than willing to comment unfavorably on almost anybody, especially after he'd had a few drinks. He loved to put one foot on the brass rail, give his cigar an expansive wave and let loose with both barrels. I remember one night in his favorite Denver saloon, Buchanan's. The usual crowd of talkers and drinkers was assembled when Grampa spoke up, "It's strange the Democratic party chose that name. After all, their main claim to fame is fighting a long war dedicated to saving slavery. On the other hand, their competitors don't have much to recommend them. You can't get a sheet of cigarette paper between what the Democrats and Republicans stand for — they're all fugitives from common decency."

One of the bystanders made the mistake of encouraging him. "Are you trying to say that politics isn't important? Our whole country depends on our political leaders!"

Grampa took a drink and started to warm to his subject, "Political leaders? Those third-raters would sell their immortal souls, if they had any, for a chance to prance around in the spotlight while somebody else pays the bills. I'm in favor of the write-in ballot myself. If we've got to vote, might as well vote for Cicero, George Washington, Robert E. Lee — somebody worthwhile. If we can't find a live statesman, at least we should pick a first-class corpse!"

Grampa Stewart was generous to a fault — and the next moment could be arrogant and self-centered. He blew hot and cold, had a sharp tongue, no interest in anybody else's opinion, and a constant restlessness as he reached out for that fortune always just around the corner. He was a gifted man and he taught me a lot about the world.

I suppose it's odd that two of the people who taught me the most and who had such an influence on my life should be so very different as Grammaw Hagee and Grampa Stewart. Certainly they never got on well. Maybe they weren't really so different. They both were pieces of a tough, self-reliant nineteenth-century frontier. They both found

themselves sojourning in the twentieth century where neither felt much at home.

Chalk Creek Gulch

Grampa Stewart didn't come to Denver often when I was a kid. Business did bring him down from the high country one day in 1914. He swooped by our house in South Denver mostly to see me. By the time his visit was over the idea had occurred to him that I should go along on a "business trip" for a few days. He tried the idea on me first and when he got an enthusiastic reception he went to work on my folks. They were a little spooky about it, because nobody ever knew for sure what kind of "business" Grampa Stewart had in mind.

"I've got to look at a mine up Chalk Creek Gulch. We can take the train right here from Denver. The Denver South Park and Pacific runs up the Gulch and we can stop at Woodstock, no more than a couple miles from the mine. Shouldn't take more than a few days for the whole trip. I'll bring him back good as new. It'll be a great experience for the boy."

My folks were never confident that trips with Grampa Stewart were "a great experience for a young boy," but he wasn't much for being told no. An hour later we were packed and on our way — the twelve-year-old boy and the tall, lanky, bearded old Scotsman with the black coat and the heavy cane. His white hair tended to stand up in the wind as we walked. He would give it an occasional impatient smoothing pat as he hurried on his way, but he never paused long enough to stop talking.

We rode the streetcar to downtown Denver and Union Station, where we boarded a train that would have us in the Gulch in time for bed late that night. The ride into the mountains was something I still remember, winding up

Turkey Creek Canyon, down Crow Hill to Bailey, up through Grant, over Kenosha Pass, and arriving at that special place where you can see for miles across the great mountain-locked meadow of South Park. The train went on across the Park, over Trout Creek Pass, down the Arkansas Valley to Chalk Creek, west into the Gulch between Mount Princeton and Mount Antero, where the mountains stand guard over the great continental watershed dividing the country into east and west.

We stayed that night at the Antero Hotel, built in the mouth of the Gulch at the point where the great hot springs rise from beneath the mountains. All the way from Denver Grampa Stewart had been talking, sometimes to me, sometimes to other passengers, most often to the crowd clustered in the cigar smoke around the bar at the end of the last car on the train. He had discussed politics, religion, mining, feminism, and the future of the Republic, all by the time we arrived at the Big Hotel. As usual, I hadn't followed everything Grampa Stewart had said, but that didn't make any difference to him. By the time we left the train at the Big Hotel, Grampa Stewart had consumed a huge amount of alcohol. It seemed not to interfere with his talking. It didn't even interfere with his walking. He marched into the Big Hotel as if he owned the place and set us up with a room for the night. The mine he was being paid to examine was still some twenty miles up the Gulch, but he had decided to stop at the Big Hotel and not chance the accommodations at the tiny railside stop of Woodstock. As it turned out, Grampa was right as usual. The lawyer who owned the mine had stopped at the Big Hotel on an earlier train that afternoon. The "mining engineer" and his client soon found each other and spent the balance of the evening in the bar. I wasn't sure that anybody would be ready to go up the Gulch the next morning. I'd seen Grampa Stewart looking better, but he was up and around and ready to be on his way when the train arrived at mid-morning.

The trip through the mountains on the way up from Denver had been beautiful, but it paled before our passage up the Gulch. I'd never seen the place before and I found myself looking up from the Big Hotel as we waited for the train. Above me a gigantic wall of limestone formed one whole face of Mount Princeton. The Chalk Cliffs were named from the strange pale color of that limestone. Chalk Creek got its name because every heavy rainstorm eroded those soft limestone cliffs and turned the creek milky white as the runoff descended the mountain. That soft limestone eroded so quickly that it had produced a wild array of cathedral spires sculpted in white stone — quite a sight for a young boy standing on the train platform in the clear morning light.

The train ride up the Gulch went through the narrow pass between Princeton and Antero, climbing higher and higher along a roadbed carved in the shoulder of Antero and running high above the creek in the valley below. That old roadbed, from which the tracks have now been so long removed, ran through some of the most spectacular high country in the Rockies, winding upward into places where trains probably weren't meant to go. The trouble was, nineteenth-century men never understood they weren't supposed to go there with their railroad. In those days, progress went everywhere. It was an article of faith. They were too tough to be beaten and too much children of their age to ask why.

We finally arrived at Woodstock and made a deal for several horses to take us up the side of the mountain to the shaft Grampa Stewart was to inspect. Most of those small mines back in the hills were tiny one- and two-man operations and tough to reach. The narrow tunnels were usually drilled into the rock with "single-jacks" or "double-jacks," one or two men using hammer and drill to challenge the mountain. Food, tools, and survival gear had to be hauled up the mountain on their backs. They braved the elements, battled the mountain, and fought for life itself. Most of them didn't know enough to be afraid. They believed in progress with a capital P. More important, they believed in themselves. A little dynamite didn't hurt, either. That's what blasted out the solid rock which stood in their way. The tunnels they blasted were shored up with timber cut around the mineshaft opening. Those timbers were placed by hand. The narrow shafts they built far back under the mountains were dangerous, made still more dangerous by the tricks that geology and underground water can play. Just going underground in one of those tunnels was more of a chance than most people take in their entire lives.

This shaft was no different from all the rest. We finally arrived high on the face of the mountain, looking almost straight down to the valley below. We found the campsite built next to an outcropping of rock where a small stream of underground water surfaced to form a pool caught in a hollow of the hillside. The tunnel ran back into the hill and then slanted downward as it followed the "color," the trail of precious metal running toward the main vein. At least the lawyer who owned the mine hoped the main vein was there, somewhere. He had already spent more than he could afford and wanted an expert opinion on what to do now. That was Grampa Stewart's job. He spent the first day collecting samples here and there, in the mine shaft and outside on the face of the mountain. Finally he rolled up his sleeves and went back into the mine where he began tunneling a small opening at right angles to the work already done. I watched him prepare the dynamite, cutting one of those yellow sticks in half with a jackknife. Then he cut a length of black blasting cord and connected the two with a cap of fulminate of mercury. "George, you don't have to worry about dynamite and you don't have to worry about the fuse, but you better watch that fulminate of mercury or it'll blow your head off."

Grampa Stewart blasted half a dozen times that day as he worked farther and farther back on his new angle for the tunnel. As he worked, he gathered his samples. By the end of the second day we were ready to go back down the mountain and take the samples to the assayer's office.

I think that trip up the mountain never amounted to anything. At least I never heard any more about it. But seeing the Gulch for the first time and that leathery old man in operation is still a vivid memory. We went back down the Gulch to Buena Vista, where Grampa Stewart put me on a train for Denver. He stayed on to catch his own train north to Leadville. My folks gave me a close look when I got home, checking for any signs of damage or corruption, but I was apparently about the same as when I left. Except for my one-day outing with Grammaw Hagee when she inspected the mine above Idaho Springs, that was about all my mining experience until I returned from the navy.

The St. Louis

One day in 1920, not too long after I had come back from the navy, Grampa Stewart came to town with one of those "deals" that he seemed always to have going. He came at a good time for me. I was a child of the twenties ready to make my fortune. And that fortune was waiting just around the corner.

Grampa Stewart and I were out on South Broadway at Buchanan's. Billy Bonnie and I had met him downtown earlier that afternoon. The three of us worked our way out South Broadway, stopping at a few saloons on the way and finally arriving at Grampa Stewart's favorite. Buchanan's was a survivor from the days when saloons were really saloons — a great dark mahogany bar, a floor of tiny tiles forming complicated mosaic patterns, and bartenders that poured an honest drink.

Grampa was busy explaining his latest deal. "Leadville is booming. Mining is going to be Colorado's future and Leadville is in the absolute center of the best mining country in the state. Gold and silver are there for the taking. All it takes is a little imagination."

Another drink, a cigar, and Grampa Stewart was warming to his subject. "You know why slaves don't rebel? Why weary husbands stay with their wives? Why people stay in the same old jobs? Why most men stay chained to their hateful destiny? I'll tell you why — lack of imagination!"

The current vision was a deal Grampa Stewart was negotiating to "bring in" a new mine. It was to be a fifty-fifty partnership, with a Leadville merchant supplying the money and Grampa Stewart contributing the professional mining experience. "George, this one can't miss. What makes a man is to take a step, then another step. You have to keep taking the next step. It's time for that in your life. Come to Leadville and help me bring in this mine."

By the time we left Buchanan's that night, the decision was made. I was on my way to Leadville to make a fortune. Within a week I stepped off a train in Leadville and met Grampa Stewart and Uncle Jake. It was mid-January in a mountain-mining town two miles above sea level. I never saw so much snow. It was six feet on the level with drifts higher than the telegraph poles. Enough of the board sidewalks had been shoveled to make a path along the downtown streets. Grampa Stewart, Jake, and I made our way to the nearest bar where the gambling and drinking were already wide open at midday. As we stood at the bar for our first drink, the floor beneath us began to shake as the air filled with a distant roar. Nobody seemed to pay much attention, so I waited until the floor stopped shaking before I asked whether we had just survived an earthquake. The bartender laughed, "No, just a snowslide in the hills — happens all the time this time of year. That snow has to go somewhere."

Leadville was still a frontier town, at least a full generation behind Denver in its self-conscious civilization. The town had been birthed with the discovery of some enormous silver deposits in 1877. By 1880 it had become the biggest silver boom camp the American West would ever know. Those early days brought the prospectors and the miners and the inevitable population of a frontier town, but they also produced some colorful characters who wanted Leadville to be a special place in its own right. Perhaps the most famous of these was Horace Tabor, a Leadville storekeeper who built an enormous fortune from the miners he grubstaked. He then spent that fortune on Leadville's Grand Hotel and the Tabor Opera House. Tabor was long gone by the time I was on hand in 1920, but Grampa Stewart pointed out the Opera House as we trudged along the narrow paths shoveled through the mountains of snow looming over us. Grampa shared another of his endless opinions as we passed the Opera House. He told Jake and me that he couldn't understand why people took the opera so seriously. "For my part, I never saw one of those Wagnerian beauties that was anything but a blimp fitted with a calliope." On our way to Grampa's house, the boardwalks twice more shook under the impact of snow crashing down the hills that flanked the town.

Some of the wild and woolly days had passed and things were much quieter than they used to be, but Leadville was still a frontier town in 1920. As we stopped at one more saloon on the way home, Grampa Stewart started filling me in on the local color. He was especially fond of telling the story of a Leadville undertaker who had so much business during a pneumonia epidemic in 1900 that he couldn't make the new caskets fast enough. It seems he solved the problem by digging up the coffins of some of his recent customers and reselling them. Grampa Stewart took a big puff on his cigar and grinned, "He was doing fine until somebody got suspicious and a vigilante committee caught him replenishing his stock one night. It seems that the undertaker was asked to leave town. He's the biggest undertaker in Denver now. I think it's always interesting to know how local moguls get their start!"

That first day also showed me the saddest survivor of the old Leadville. Baby Doe, Horace Tabor's widow, had stayed on in town long after Horace and the money were gone. The beautiful Baby Doe, who had been the toast of Colorado society, had been told by Tabor on his deathbed to hold the Pittsburgh mine. It had proved worthless but the old woman still lived at the mine, coming to town with gunnysacks for shoes. Baby Doe was making one of her trips downtown the day I arrived. The Leadville storekeepers saw that she had groceries every week and even told her it was part of an inheritance that had been set aside for her care. There wasn't any inheritance, but in its own way Leadville took care of its own.

The next morning Jake and I tagged along with Grampa Stewart on his way downtown to see his new partner. Frank Zeitz ran a grocery store near the center of town and had a reputation as a successful, if slightly sharp, trader. He had bankrolled several other successful mining ventures, and his had been a natural place for Grampa Stewart to turn when he developed his idea about the St. Louis. Several miles west of Leadville, in an area that had undergone considerable prospecting but no really big strikes, Grampa Stewart had been nosing around and had become con-

vinced that a major gold deposit was waiting. If true, such a deposit would be very unusual for Leadville, because the area was primarily a center for silver mining. But the more Grampa Stewart studied the area, the more sure he became that a major gold strike was there waiting. He was smart enough to keep this to himself until he'd done all his homework and was ready to visit Frank Zeitz. Zeitz knew Grampa by reputation and was ready to make a deal. His bankroll gave us more than enough to take care of everything we needed to do.

Starting in mid-January with the surface work still ahead of us, there wasn't much to be done at the site until the spring thaw. Grampa Stewart used the time to gather his findings and pick the place to run the tunnel. Once he knew where he was going, the next step was to stake a mining claim big enough to bracket the spot where the actual shaft would be. This was tricky, because Grampa couldn't be absolutely sure of the exact location for his shaft. It also was tricky because whenever a professional mining man takes a serious interest in a particular area, the secret is hard to keep. That's why Grampa let Frank Zeitz do all the filing. Even so, other people became interested and started nosing around. This worried Grampa Stewart a lot until late spring finally arrived in Leadville and we got to work. From then on, Jake and I earned our keep. Two strong young backs were a big asset to the old mining engineer.

We watched this tough old man with his white hair blowing in the wind, working day after day at a pace most younger men couldn't keep. He knew his trade, and step by step ran a tunnel into the mountain, pursuing the gold that he knew had to be there.

The St. Louis "came in" in late June. It was one of those rare mines with "free gold," nuggets of pure gold coming straight from the ground so pure that no smelting was necessary. An incredibly rich mine, the St. Louis promised wealth beyond our wildest dreams. Even now, a half century later, if you visit the mining museum in Denver, most of the samples of free gold are labeled St. Louis.

The shaft work was pretty tricky. Hard-rock mining around Leadville always had special problems and the St. Louis was worse than usual. The tunnels were narrow and dangerous. The constant threat of underground water on various levels made it chancy whether or not the tunnel system could be protected. None of this fazed Grampa Stewart, but Jake and I were never happier than when we came back above ground at night. As for Grampa Stewart's partner, Frank Zeitz never would go underground in that tunnel for any reason.

By July 4, it was obvious that we had made a major strike. The high grade we were bringing home was so rich that sometimes we'd sort it on the living-room floor at night, selecting the gold to be sent directly to the mint. Each morning we'd bring the high grade to Zeitz to be sent on to the mint in Denver.

Grampa Stewart was a strange prospector. So long as he was looking for gold, the fever was on him. He would work long and hard to reach his dream, but the minute he was sure that the gold was there, he would start to lose interest and begin sniffing around for something more exciting.

Something more exciting for him turned out to be his decision to take the whole family on a trip around the world. For this nineteenth-century man, a trip around the world was the proof that he had really arrived. Jake, Uncle Phil, dad, and all the family were invited to take the trip. By August 1, 1920, the plans were taking shape. Grampa Stewart went down to see his partner to draw an advance on what had already been processed from the mine. I wasn't in the room when it happened, but when Grampa Stewart went into Frank Zeitz's office, he discovered that there had been only one gentleman in the gentlemen's agreement. He was a very well paid mining engineer, but he wasn't half owner in the St. Louis. The deal had been done on a handshake and no legal records existed to substantiate Grampa's claim. There would be no trek around the world.

Grampa Stewart came straight home that night. He was a little paler than usual and said almost nothing, except that the trip was off. During the next month we worked harder than we had worked when we brought in the mine, following step by step the careful plans of the canny old Scot. Grampa Stewart completely redrew the charts of the St. Louis mine. Bit by bit we retunneled and restructured until the high-grade pockets were entirely lost in the maze of hard-rock tunneling and underground water. On September 3 Grampa Stewart walked into Frank Zeitz's office. Jake and I were with him this time. Zeitz looked up from his desk, "Hello, Walt. What can I do for you today?"

Grampa Stewart looked him straight in the eye and without so much as batting an eyelash said, "I found the St. Louis once, you son of a bitch, now you find it. I quit."

Hard-rock mining is a funny business, much complicated by underground water and narrow, twisting shafts. Frank Zeitz invested more money in his search for the St. Louis than he had taken out of it in the first place. Grampa Stewart stayed on in Leadville and watched the entire process with gloating satisfaction. He always told us that the high grade was still there and that he knew how to find it. Jake and I knew he was right.

I learned a couple of things from all this. For one thing, I learned about "gentlemen's agreements." You need two gentlemen to make them a success.

The editor of the Leadville paper got interested in the story and wanted Grampa Stewart to tell the whole thing for his readers. That was something he was never willing to do. After asking him several times, the editor of the paper finally lost his temper. "Walt, what's the matter with you? Why in hell don't you want to tell this story?"

By then Grampa was also losing his temper. He shouted, "Because newspapers are a preparatory school for the insane asylum, and I have better things to do with my time."

Somehow, no matter how hard everybody tried, none could ever find the mold that fitted Grampa Stewart.

Wobblies

Nothing ever kept Grampa down for long. By Halloween, he had been offered a job as superintendent of a mine twenty miles back in the hills above Leadville. The terrain leading to the mine was tough enough to make it necessary to build a completely self-sufficient operation on the mine site, complete with commissary, two boardinghouse saloons, and all the necessary mine offices. One small handcar, running on jerrybuilt narrow-gauge tracks, provided all the supplies and one trip a day into and out of Leadville.

With the St. Louis, my fortune had disappeared around the corner again and I didn't have anything to do for the moment, so I took a job at the new mine and was with Grampa when he arrived at the Argonaut as the new superintendent. I don't know what I expected, but when we finally arrived on the handcar, all I saw were a series of buildings made of 1 x 6 boards covered with tarpaper. The owners had been putting their money into the mine, and the accommodations above ground didn't amount to much.

In the early twenties, the Wobblies, the Industrial Workers of the World, big Bill Haywood's old union, had become pretty active again and were up to their old tricks, playing very rough in their attempt to organize the mines and bring the owners down. Leadville was no exception.

The Wobblies had targeted the Argonaut as their point of entry into Leadville, maybe because it was so isolated and so dependent on a single source of outside transportation. Certainly the Argonaut was far enough from the law that all of us up there were entirely on our own.

That was one of the main reasons that Grampa Stewart had been hired as superintendent. He was a good mining engineer and his reputation spoke for itself, but he also had a reputation as a hard man who wouldn't back away from a fight. Any new superintendent at the Argonaut had to expect a fight. The last two superintendents had disappeared underground and never resurfaced. Everybody knew the Wobblies were responsible, but nobody said so out loud. The Argonaut camp was about equally divided between the nonunion men and the Wobblies. Each side had its boardinghouse and saloon. Tension hung in the air like dynamite waiting to explode.

Over the next few weeks, Grampa went into the mine, always with two bodyguards, one ahead and one behind, each carrying a sawed-off shotgun. The Argonaut had been suffering from some Wobblie sabotage, but Grampa was a steadying presence with the men and he knew what had to be done. Within a month the mine was producing well and the trouble seemed past. The Wobblies were sullen, but quiet.

A couple of days before Christmas we learned that the Wobblies had only been biding their time. It was about eight o'clock in the evening when a dynamite blast shook the nonunion boardinghouse and saloon. One whole corner of the kitchen at the back of the boardinghouse lifted off the ground and blew off in all directions. Every window in the place was breaking around us as we all hit the floor. Grampa was the first man up, rushing out the front door and around the boardinghouse toward the location of the blast. Several of us were right behind him. It took time to sort through the wreckage where the kitchen had been. Buried in the rubble was an unmistakable story for anybody used to handling dynamite. A whole sack of those yellow sticks had been planted in a row along the back of the building, but only the first stick had exploded. The Wobblies were trying to blow us all to Kingdom Come, but a bad fuse bought us a reprieve.

We came back in out of the cold and the deep snow. Everybody knew what had really happened, but we were all waiting to see what happened next. Grampa Stewart took his gun belt from the wall and buckled it around his waist. "Boys, the Wobblies tried to blow us up tonight. That's the last time it's going to happen. Get your guns and come with me."

Before the night was over, no Wobblies were left in camp. Maybe the failure of the dynamite blast left the Wobblies without alternative plans. Maybe they were so surprised to see us alive that they lost their nerve. I don't know. I do know they didn't put up any real fight. They were so scared when we charged through the front door of the union boardinghouse carrying our guns that they grabbed the belongings closest to them and beat a retreat down the narrow-gauge tracks toward Leadville. Nobody said a word. That twenty-mile walk must have been long and cold, but none of them wanted to spend the night in camp.

We moved into the Wobbly boardinghouse that night because it was in a lot better shape than our place. Grampa Stewart opened the bar and we drank Wobbly liquor most of the night.

That night broke the back of the Wobblies in Leadville. The Argonaut became a paying proposition and Walt Stewart became the toast of the town. We stayed there the rest of the winter until Grampa Stewart started getting a little too prosperous. That always made him itchy. He was

better at looking for his fortune than at enjoying it. And that's probably why he started looking around again for something else to do. He found it in late spring 1921.

Leadville and the hills were beginning to emerge from beneath their deep winter blanket. Jake and I put Grampa Stewart on a train running south to Buena Vista, down the Arkansas Valley and alongside the towering Saguache mountains. He was on his way back to the Gulch I had visited with him years ago. As usual, he was looking at another mining operation where he thought a good opportunity was waiting. Jake and I stood on the platform and waved as the train pulled out, not knowing how close we were to losing Grampa that day.

Bits and pieces of the story came back later. Apparently what happened is that an efficiency engineer from the Denver and Rio Grande central office was at the throttle on that trip down the Arkansas Valley. He was testing a new malley-compound, a double-boilered engine with sixteen drive wheels, the biggest and most powerful steam locomotive ever made. The regular engineer who knew the run south was also in the cab, but the efficiency engineer was there for this first special run and was in charge. The regular knew the winding course along the Arkansas and the steep grade on the way down to Buena Vista, but the "expert" didn't. He was out to make a name for himself. Despite repeated warnings from the regular engineer, the efficiency expert pushed the engine and the train far faster than the usual run. Near Granite, rounding a turn above the Arkansas River, the train left the track, spewing cars and people into and across the Arkansas. That day was the worst wreck in Denver and Rio Grande Railroad history.

As usual, Grampa Stewart had been standing at the bar at the rear of the last car on the train. That was probably what saved him. He wasn't sure what happened, but he told us the first thing he remembered was walking down the track toward Granite. Below him were cars and people, scattered down the steep hillside and into the river below. Apparently, he had been thrown from the train and had hit the ground on the grass next to the roadbed. He stayed on to help patch up the passengers who were still alive and finally hitched a ride back to Leadville late that night. We first saw him standing in the door of the house, dressed in his usual black suit, covered with mud and blood. He had a big cut across his forehead and he had lost his cane, but otherwise didn't seem much the worse for wear. As he stood in the living room with a drink in his hand, he wondered aloud why so many people had been killed and others had been spared. I remember his words that night as we went upstairs to bed, "The gods are a vicious lot most of the time, but once in a while they do show an unmistakable sense of humor!"

The Mary Murphy

It wasn't long until Grampa Stewart was ready to go again. When opportunity knocked, he always got impatient. The opportunity he had been on his way to find in the Gulch was the Mary Murphy mine. The Mary Murphy had been a big silver strike in the 1880s. Five miners in partnership had brought in the big strike and then had used their money to build the Big Hotel twenty miles below at the mouth of the Gulch, the same hotel where I stayed as a boy years before, during my first visit to the Gulch with Grampa Stewart.

The Mary Murphy, long since in receivership, was located far up Chalk Creek Gulch and all but completely abandoned. Grampa Stewart had been eyeing the mine and thought he saw the way to get back on the main silver vein and make the Mary Murphy a paying proposition. As usual, all he needed was some cash to put the venture together and he had several Leadville backers who were willing to bet on his track record. This time he was being a little smarter and was treating the investors as limited partners. Ownership of the strike, if developed, would be firmly in Grampa's hands.

As we rode up the Gulch on the train on an early summer day in 1921, Grampa was especially expansive. He waved that ever-present cigar out the window and told Jake and me, "Take a look at some of the most beautiful country you'll ever see. This Gulch is really God's country. You know Mark Twain visited here about the time he was writing *Roughing It*. He loved the country. In fact, he talked the mine superintendent at the Mary Murphy into taking him on a handcar ride all the way down the grade to the Big Hotel. The only trouble was, they got to going so fast that the handcar ran away. The only thing that saved them was that Twain was smart enough to tie an Irishman on the end of a rope and throw him out for ballast. Slowed 'em down and saved Twain's life.

"I believe when you take a look at the mine, boys, you're going to see the opportunity of a lifetime. You know the trouble with most people is that they live in a dark, self-enclosed prison. They're so busy looking down that they never see that wide, wonderful universe out there. That's where the opportunity is! You know, I've never really thought about it before, but have you noticed that every time anything really creative comes along, you can count on all the powers of hell and all the do-gooders in the world to rise up and say that it can't happen. Despite all that mealy-mouthed claptrap, good opportunities *do* come and good things *do* happen. But remember that they happen only because somebody is finally tough enough to stand up and do the job.

"There's an old story about the parting of the Red Sea for Moses. The Talmud says that the waters of the Red

Sea didn't part until one man *believed* Moses and plunged in. It's when somebody's willing to plunge in that things really get started.

"Sometimes you can lose. That fellow that plunged into the Red Sea might've drowned you know. But God offers us all the same deal — take what you want, take it and then pay for it."

By the time that day had ended and we'd looked at the Mary Murphy, I was so full of Grampa Stewart's optimism that I was ready to take what I wanted — and thought I could pay for it. I came in with him as a partner on that wild venture at the Mary Murphy. We just couldn't convince Uncle Jake that he ought to stay. In fact, I argued that night until I was blue in the face, but the next day he left for Denver, determined that his real opportunity was waiting for him somewhere out in the big world. His head was full of the Roaring Twenties and his mining days were over.

The original cabin on the claim site was still standing. It had been built before the Mary Murphy was discovered. High on the side of the mountain and on the other side of the Mary Murphy itself, the old cabin appealed to Grampa. As soon as he saw the old place, he decided to fix it up as our base of operations. It meant a long trip around the face of the mountain each day to reach the diggings, but somehow the old cabin looked like the right place. As I went to work on it, I had no idea I was putting together the home where I would spend much of the rest of my life.

We went right to work and had enough money from the Leadville backers to hire a fair-sized crew while Grampa started his exploratory work. I'd learned so much from him in the past year that I was getting to be a real help running the men and the mining operation. We worked like dogs that summer of 1921. Before the snow flew that

fall, Grampa Stewart had done it again, relocating the main silver property and remaking the Mary Murphy into a very valuable mining property. The vein was so rich that we expanded the crew to a full-time mining operation and continued to work through the winter. That winter I learned what work really meant. We continued work for another full year. By the time another spring had come to the Rockies, I was a wealthy young man. In May 1923, I left Grampa Stewart at the mine for a few days while I made a trip to Denver on business. While I was there I stopped by to see my other special person in all the world, Grammaw Hagee. For all of her grumpy pessimism, Grammaw Hagee also had that nineteenth-century optimistic frontier streak, and she was dying to hear what I'd been doing. I painted such a glowing picture in her little house by the South Platte that I convinced her to come back with me and visit the mine. I was always trying to get my two favorite people together, although I never had much luck.

On the train ride back to the Gulch, Grammaw Hagee began telling me a story about Grampa Stewart, something I had never heard in all the years I had been around those two. "Walt Stewart likes to have everybody think that he is the toughest man in the world and doesn't care about anyone or anything. But, George, one time when he thought your dad was dying, he locked himself in a hotel room in Denver and refused to come out for anyone until he heard from the hospital. All that night he kept the lights burning. But when your father got past the crisis the next morning, Walt sent him such insulting telephone messages that the nurse refused to relay them. Walt's not so tough as he likes everybody to think he is. He's just an old humbug."

Right from the start, the visit looked as though it were doomed for failure. Grammaw looked around the cabin disapprovingly, and before you knew it, the two of them were in an argument about drinking, God, and practically anything else you could name.

"Honestly, Walter Stewart, I don't see how a grown man can live in as much dirt as you have in this cabin. Why if you cleaned up all the dirt in here and sent it to the smelter, we'd all be rich."

"Ellen, it's not a man's house that counts, it's what's in his soul."

"Precisely," Grammaw Hagee snapped, "a man has to think of someone besides himself once in a while. A little philanthropy is good for the soul."

"Nonsense, my dear Ellen, there is no such thing as philanthropy. It's purely an imaginary quality like being a demi-virgin or having one drink. Besides, even if you're right, when I think of the disagreeable people who I'm told have gone to a better world, I'm not sure that isn't a good argument to lead a very different kind of life."

"For all your talk about demi-virgins and one drink, there's no danger of your ever having *one* drink. Unless you change your ways, Walter Black Stewart, there's not very much doubt about where you're going to go and it won't be to a better place."

"Give me no temperance lectures, woman! Do you think God has no better way of judging a man's soul than giving him a blood test? God cares about our souls, not our stomachs. I'll grant that alcohol never got a man to heaven, but I don't believe it's grounds for keeping him out. God's not your monopoly — or mine. Drink or not, just as you like, but make sure you don't spend too much time judging your fellow men. That's God's job — and if He's half the Creator I think He is, He can handle Judgment Day without any help from you."

All this squabbling left me gaping at these two old people I loved so much. As I look back on it, I think it bothered me much more than it bothered either of them. I knew it couldn't last for long and the night of the big electrical storm terminated Grammaw Hagee's visit for certain. We had one of those unnerving storms in which the charges of electricity were so great in the high mountains that great balls of St. Elmo's fire ran across the blankets on the bed and jumped across the metal surface of the stove. One of those storms is enough to scare anybody to death. Grammaw Hagee was no sissy, but she kept repeating that if she ever got out of there alive, she would never return. And she didn't. The next morning I took her back to Denver myself. The train ride back was so friendly and chatty, it was as though nothing had happened. As we were leaving the cabin early that morning to make our way to the railhead, even Grammaw Hagee and Grampa Stewart had a few civil words for each other. I guess I never understood what was going on in their heads. Certainly I never understood the relationship those two oldtimers had.

Bedside Manner

I think I told you once that Grampa Stewart had done a stretch in medical school at McGill University. That helped him when he was back in the hills at a mine site far from a doctor. The accidents and the occasional violence of a hard life often brought casualties requiring first aid on the spot. Grampa Stewart seemed always to know what to do. After a while, you got used to his doctoring a body on the kitchen table.

To understand the kind of doctoring he did, you would have to understand the kind of people who worked those mines. Tough they had to be, with stamina to withstand the exposure that would send an ordinary person to a hospital with pneumonia. Every day they challenged death, with dangerous equipment and dangerous conditions, especially underground. They were tough and they were proud of it. They played as hard as they worked. Pour a few slugs of whiskey into men like that and you're likely to find that every one of them gets the idea that he can lick any man in the house. Put a couple dozen men like that together, give them all enough whiskey to liven things up, and you can count on some encounters guaranteed to produce injuries, even if everybody made it through the workday in one piece.

Doctoring a bunch like that calls for some special medical talent. Maybe it was just as well that Grampa Stewart didn't have a medical degree. Dealing with some of those rough and ignorant bozos demanded a different touch. These tough men with their dangerous work and rough personal lives seemed to have something about them that was already fading fast in older, more established eastern society. In their own elemental way, they were loyal to one another and to the life they led.

One miner, battered and bruised in a cave-in and pressing his hand against several badly cracked ribs, was sitting on the edge of our kitchen table when we came through the cabin door one evening at dusk. "Are you hurt much?" Grampa asked him.

"Well, not bad. Nothin' a drink of whiskey won't fix." Grampa Stewart laid him down and gave him one of his best bandaging jobs. "You bandaged me so damn tight, I can't bend."

"You're not supposed to bend, you damn fool. That's why I bandaged you in the first place. Besides, it's too good an opportunity to miss. Bandaging's kind of a pleasure, it's so clean and efficient and neat—not at all like messing with a man's innards. Have another drink and you'll feel better."

After two more drinks, the patient asked the doctor, "What's the matter with me?"

"I'll tell you, bud. You got more bruises on you than if somebody had slugged you with a baseball bat. You broke

a couple of ribs, you've lost some blood, you're probably suffering from shock, and there's not a single solitary damn thing wrong with you that another drink and a good night's sleep won't cure."

So much for bedside manner.

Another time Grampa Stewart and I were down at the Big Hotel when a girl was brought in who'd been shot. She was a tiny thing and Grampa labored long and hard to patch her up as best he could for the trip to town and a real sawbones. As he worked, he and I kept trying to get her to tell us who had shot her, but she wouldn't answer. About two months later we saw the same little girl on the street in Buena Vista. She came up and thanked Grampa for saving her life. She also told us the reason she wouldn't say who had shot her. It seems her husband had gunned her that night and had been standing right behind us all the time Grampa was working on her. She said her husband had his hand on his gun and had been ready to kill her and shoot Grampa too if the truth had come out. Grampa tipped his hat and thanked her for having repaid the favor so graciously by telling us the story. "Now, George, let's visit the Green Parrot, have a drink, and celebrate our good fortune on still being alive."

That day at the Green Parrot we ran into one of the two doctors in Buena Vista, a man who cordially detested Grampa for his occasional semipro forays into the medical field. Grampa warmly reciprocated that dislike and often took the opportunity to tell the good doctor that he was a quack. This frontier medical practitioner was better than half drunk and was overflowing with good spirits. For once he wanted to bury the hatchet. He reckoned without Grampa Stewart's unlimited Scottish persistence at bad humor.

The doctor was drunk enough to wobble a little as he leaned against the bar announcing to my grandfather and

to the barroom in general, "It makes no difference what anybody in this town thinks of me, because I've decided to leave the practice of medicine. I'm on my way to Denver to take up a new career and a major new business opportunity as an undertaker."

Grampa laid his cigar on the bar to stick out his hand and announce, "Congratulations, I'm happy that you haven't seen fit to change your profession."

"Come, my dear Mr. Stewart, surely you must be jesting."

"I do not jest with humorless men," replied Grampa Stewart. We had a drink on that, in fact several more drinks, and then went to dinner across the street at the Buena Vista Hotel.

Doctoring wasn't the big reason for our being in the Gulch. We were busy making a success of the Mary Murphy. And we made a big success. By summer 1923 we were making money hand over fist. As usual when things were going well, Grampa Stewart started to look for something more exciting. This time I was all for it. The twenties were beginning to roar. Denver was a boomtown. Jake had already started to make a success of his trip to the big city. Grampa Stewart and I had the wanderlust and way more money than we could spend. Put it all together and you can understand why we decided it was time to take another look at Denver.

The twenties were roaring and I was listening. I was sure that something was waiting there more important than anything else we had done so far. Grampa Stewart wasn't so sure, but he never was one to wait around when there was something new to try.

V
'TIS A PRIVILEGE

Denver changed after World War I. As the twenties arrived, the little cow town became a city. An age was ending and a new age was aching to be born.

The daily weather report on the front page of the *Denver Post* told readers, "'Tis a Privilege to Live in Colorado." The snow might be six feet deep in the passes. The plains might be trapped in the hottest, driest summer in years. The *Post* and its readers still believed there was no place like Colorado.

That enthusiasm extended far beyond the weather. Colorado was God's country and Coloradans were special people. With all the hoopla that made the twenties, the people of Colorado announced their superiority to the world. World War I had pointed the way: the Age of the Press Agent was at hand. The *Post* offered prizes for the largest trout caught in a Colorado stream, the oldest pioneer, the newest Colorado baby, and every other conceivable "largest," "most," "youngest," and "oldest" the press agents could dream up. Colorado congratulated itself on the tallest mountains, the most mountains, the best weather, the purest air. God's handiwork itself became an item of personal property for Colorado.

The twenties ballyhoo brought a raft of nutty projects to Denver. Art Hammond and I were standing in the crowd on a bright summer morning in 1923 when Gene Bedini gazed upward and waited, fork in mouth, for a turnip to be thrown from the twelfth floor of the Foster Building. We all cheered when Bedini performed as advertised, spearing the speeding turnip midflight a few feet above the streets of downtown Denver. That particular item was a typical *Denver Post* promotion. Sometimes the promotions worked, sometimes they didn't. But one thing was certain: the *Post* was always center-ring when it came to ballyhoo.

One of the *Post* reporters, a woman named Polly Pry, had used the ballyhoo power of the *Post* to procure a second trial for the convicted murderer and cannibal Alfred Packer. Some years before, in a silver strike in the San Juan mountains in southwestern Colorado, Packer had killed and eaten his fellow prospectors during a lonely, starving winter when they had all been trapped in a cave after a heavy snowstorm. Even in frontier days cannibalism was frowned on, and Packer had gone to the state pen. Thanks to the efforts of Polly Pry and the ballyhoo of the twenties, Packer was given a second trial.

Polly Pry's principal argument, as it appeared in the pages of the *Denver Post*, was that a man should not be made to suffer forever simply because he made the one small mistake of killing and eating seven of his friends. The second trial was a real showpiece. Packer was already a self-confessed murderer and cannibal, so the second trial centered entirely on matters of character and how he had been a model prisoner during his stay in Canyon City. This early-day sociological jurisprudence finally secured Packer's release and he spent the balance of his life as bodyguard for the publishers of the *Denver Post*, Fred Bonfils and Harry Tammen. The entrance to the publishers' offices at the *Post* was done entirely in red velvet and had acquired a nickname: the Bucket of Blood. Packer would sit in that red velvet hallway, tipped back in a chair against the wall and holding a sawed-off shotgun across his lap. He twice took bullets intended for one of the publishers of the *Post* and became a curiosity on the Denver scene, proving that a reformed cannibal could still be a model citizen, at least in Denver in the 1920s.

Another annual *Post* promotion was a special Union Pacific train carrying prominent Denverites to the Cheyenne Frontier Days. The cowboys, Indians, and bucking broncos, plus an endless supply of free food, liquor, and dancing girls, managed to delight and stupefy most of the Denver business, political, and professional leadership for the better part of a week each year. The Union Pacific always made available its crack Denver-Chicago train, the Columbine Limited, especially for the occasion. The first year I had enough money to be considered an important community leader, whatever that might be, and was invited to make the train run to Cheyenne. I raised hell along with everybody else. The second year I laid back and watched the fun. The best part was never the drunken hoopla. I had already seen plenty of that in my life and would see a whole lot more. The real pleasure was watching the country slide by going north to Cheyenne. Even in July patches of snow remained in some of the gullies on the Colorado high plains. Tumbleweeds matted against the snow fences on the way north. The train moved past little country schoolhouses, towns no more than a wide spot in the road, and cattle barns with the usual ads for chewing tobacco and liver pills. Standing on the back of the train and listening to the roar of the big party going on in the cars ahead of me, I watched the twilight grow longer and longer until the dry creek beds gave way to the lights of Wyoming's big town, filled to bursting with people, lights, and noise. Somehow I always liked the train trip better than the arrival. Standing on that back platform and watching the country go by was a reminder that not everything had changed.

The year the International Advertising Clubs of the World held their annual convention in Denver was a new high for press agentry. The Moffat Tunnel, running under the Rockies to create an east-west railroad connection, wasn't complete, but it already was being treated with the ballyhoo of the new age. The tunnel was the "longest," the "most expensive," the "most advanced." Naturally, the *Denver Post* sponsored a special train for advertising men from across the nation, hauling seven hundred fifty gentlemen of the press to the east portal of the tunnel, where a table half a mile long was set up inside the mountain. The press agents were served a "typical miners' meal" of beans, biscuits, and bacon. "Beans, biscuits, bacon, and bull," muttered Grammaw Hagee when she read the story in the *Post*.

Whether Grammaw Hagee liked it or not, Denver in the twenties was "on the move." Materialism, technology, salesmanship, and success were the order of the day. The town I'd known as a boy was slow and dull by comparison. The future beckoned to the young man who had the "drive" to reject the old ways and embrace the new. "Opportunity was just around the corner." Grampa and I already had more than enough money and the Mary Murphy was turning out more all the time. We kept expanding, acquiring more of the old silver properties where the new methods could make the mines pay. It was a fast track that kept us more than busy, but it left plenty of time to get mixed up in some of the antics that the twenties brought to Denver.

Prohibition was responsible for many of those changes, and most of them weren't for the better. One thing I know for sure — people usually don't improve a situation by driving it underground. I've watched busybodies working on variations of that scheme for my whole life, and the attempt always seems to make things worse. Prohibition was no exception.

If Denver was already colorful as a free-swinging, free-drinking ex-frontier town, it became positively scarlet in the glow created by the Eighteenth Amendment. For one thing, the town became rather trigger-happy. One outraged husband immortalized the Ship's Tavern, at the Brown Palace Hotel, by shooting a liquor dealer and would-be Lothario named Tony Van Phul. This was the husband's straightforward western way to express his disapproval of the relationship between his wife and Van Phul. It was rumored that Tony Van Phul, as he lay dying on the floor of the Ship's Tavern, was even more unhappy with the situation than the cuckolded husband. For a while after the shooting, a rash of similar news items appeared. If a prominent citizen harbored a desire to shoot somebody, the Ship's Tavern was *the* place to do the job. Naturally, this was frowned on by the police, not to mention the proprietors of the Brown Palace Hotel, but this seemed not to quench the enthusiasm of the customers, who developed quite a taste for shooting one another.

Fortunately for the Brown Palace, most of the drinking and shooting took place in more private surroundings. Denver developed its quiet hotels which served simultaneously as bordello and as refuge from the public eye for judges, senators, editors, and other prominent figures who needed a few days away from the pressures of community leadership. Here these worthies could drink and carry on to their hearts' content, secure in the knowledge that neither the Volstead Act nor public scrutiny would interrupt their rest and rehabilitation.

Even so, such drinking took its toll on society. One judge, after setting a new record of four days and five nights of nonstop revelry, *without ever having removed his evening clothes*, turned up at home in a scandalous state. The aftermath of his drinking had profound effects. While nursing a world-class hangover on his first morning back on the job, the judge muttered something about the "hair of the dog" and threw in several quick ones. As time was drawing near to convene court, the poor man found himself rapidly sliding back into a totally plastered state. This happens with even the best of them on occasion, and it was certainly happening to the judge. Fortunately his bailiff saw it coming and escorted the judge back to the chambers in time to douse him with ice water and restore his full legal dignity. A still higher price had to be paid for that hangover, however. It was rumored that, in the first two weeks after his return to the bench, the good judge was more than a little cranky and sentenced four men to death.

The saloons where my friends and I did our drinking in the happy pre-Prohibition days simply went underground and continued business as usual. About all that was required was a good working relationship with the local police and a few bootleggers. A thriving industry became even more prosperous. Besides, for most Americans, especially westerners, drinking was somehow more fun now that it was illegal.

And I was having my share of the fun. Our mining properties were growing and bringing in more than I could spend. I had plenty of time to build and race cars at Overland Park. I had time to drink with my friends—and we all did more than our share in that department. The collection of friends was larger now, but the old regulars were still on the job — Billy Bonnie, Art Hammond, Uncle Jake, and especially Grampa Stewart. There was one new addition, a mechanical engineer from Germany, Bill Wisecarver. Bill started working on my race cars at Overland Park and we soon became friends.

Bill was short and stocky, with a close-cropped, almost bullet-shaped head. He carried with him the perpetual aroma of the three basic ingredients in his life: grease, alcohol, and Copenhagen snuff. Bill was the best with cars and was a ready addition to the crew of drinkers who frequented Buchanan's, Soloman's, the Fall River cabin, and similar watering holes for several hundred miles in all directions. We used to bet with chance saloon acquaintances, the usual bet being that my specially built Ford could reach the summit of Loveland Pass faster than anything else in town. Many a drinking night ended with a race west from Denver, up into the high country and over one of the mountain passes. As we roared through the gravel switchbacks on the edge of thousand-foot drops to the trees and rocks waiting below, Bill Wisecarver would shout his drunken approval while Art Hammond fumbled to light a cigarette as he was tossed from side to side on the turns. Only Billy Bonnie, the long, angular, laconic Billy, was ever bothered by those races. He'd shut his eyes and mutter, "Tell me when we get to the top." We seldom lost those bets, and the late night Loveland Pass route was quite a moneymaker. While I'm sure he never cared about the commercial side of those trips, I expect my guardian angel must have lent a small helping hand from time to time — strictly in the interests of safety.

Another favorite entertainment was the fleecing of unsuspecting saloon customers who were foolish enough to bet on the outcome of some carefully staged beer-drinking contests. Billy Bonnie had grown into a lanky, beanpole of a man, a rail-thin specimen who looked like a skeleton in search of a good meal, but in point of fact he could consume more beer at a single sitting than any other living being. We had a regular source of income and some hilarious evenings convincing skeptics of Billy's peculiar talent.

Usually we had our fun at Buchanan's saloon on South Broadway, hoping to sucker some unsuspecting soul into the mistaken belief that anybody could drink more beer in less time than Billy Bonnie. When he felt really cocky, Billy would offer to drink *twice* the beer of any man in the house. This libido for malt liquor nearly sank the betting syndicate a time or two. It became an ironclad rule that Billy was to drink, but under no circumstances was he to talk. I drank whiskey, not beer, and functioned as Billy's business agent.

Buchanan's was a great speakeasy for these contests. That mosaic tile floor had felt the tread of Denver's heaviest drinkers for fifty years. Before that dark mahogany bar, Billy put them all away — miners, cowboys, truckers, local toughs, and ethnic drinkers of every description. One evening, the syndicate was challenged by the backers of a three-hundred-pound Indian, said to be the son of Geronimo. Billy made short work of Geronimo, Jr. After seventeen mugs in thirty-five minutes, the big Indian was reduced to a state resembling suffocation.

One member of the syndicate nearly always on hand was Art Hammond. Small, quick, given to vests and watch chains, this young promoter was another child of the twenties for whom the big chance was just around the corner. He lived in a kind of perpetual fog that kept him insulated from the world around him. One could never tell for sure whether Art had been drinking, because he acted much the same, drunk or sober.

Art was the kind who'd stop a dogfight by putting his arm between the dogs. Then he'd be amazed when one of them bit him. Art usually handled his business dealings about the same way. Not that he wasn't a great salesman. He could take a leak in your pocket while he told you it was raining — and you would believe him. It was just that it was hard for him to follow through. He had big ideas that didn't always make much sense.

His masterpiece of mismanagement was the big decision to organize a band to hire out around Denver for various civic and social events. No one ever knew for sure where Art found the band members, but most of them apparently came from an Italian neighborhood in Pueblo he visited one long weekend. He'd gone there to see a girl, but came back with an Italian band.

The Denver musical scene definitely wasn't ready for Art's mob. Art brought us all together for a special preview one night at Buchanan's. Everybody had a ripsnorting good time, but the more we drank, the harder it was to take Art's band seriously. Art was also having some personnel troubles with the band. The drummer, a fiery Sicilian, had already tried to use one of his drumsticks to disembowel the oboist. The oboist began threatening to blow everybody up with a homemade bomb, whose foolproof construction, he told us, had been learned at the knee of his sainted uncle in Palermo. As for the rest of the band, most were drunkards, a few apparently spoke no English at all, and the only two things they had in common were their hatred for one another and their hatred for Art.

"Somehow the idea seemed good in Pueblo. They really sounded good. You should have heard them."

"My dear Art," replied Grampa Stewart, "I consider it one of the great blessings of my life that I have never before heard this mangy collection of lunatics, not in Pueblo nor anywhere else on earth. My advice to you is run far and fast and leave this group to start a local chapter of the Black Hand."

Art did just that for a few days and the Italian band returned to Pueblo.

Another of Art's adventures gave him, and me, more satisfaction. Art had bought a dog from a filling station owner in Denver. The station sold Continental Oil Products, Conoco for short. This was a typical deal of Art's, the problem being that the dog, originally acquired as a watchdog, had become so mean that no one could approach him, not even the owner of the station. The filling station owner had given up trying and was happy to sell the wire-haired terrier cheap. Art had discovered a real bargain but, as usual with Art's "bargains," had run into trouble. Not even Art could coax his new possession into a car.

This is where I came in. That night at Buchanan's, Art had told us that no one could handle his new dog. I said I could, and Art promised to give me the dog if I could get him into my car. We drove to the filling station. From the moment Conoco and I laid eyes on each other, we knew we'd each found a friend. It took half an hour, but I got my new dog into the back seat.

"Well I'll be damned," said the station owner.

"What are you going to call him, George?" asked Art.

"How about Conoco?" And Conoco it was, for the next thirteen years, in the back seat of many cars, in good times and bad, always right there with me.

For weekends, Grampa Stewart and I bought a small cabin not too far from Denver, up Fall River in the mountains west of Idaho Springs. The place was supposed to be a mining claim, but we never did more than a little assessment work. Each year we drove the tunnel farther into the mountain, but we never found any real pay dirt.

Fall River and the mine did make a great place to spend a weekend. Load up the car with a few bottles of whiskey, some steaks, bacon, potatoes, and beer, and four or five of us would be off to do some mining.

Conoco would crawl under the cabin when the fireworks started. The game was to cut quarter sticks of dynamite, insert short fuses, light the fuses and throw the sticks into the air. The point was to hold the sticks long enough so that when they were thrown they would explode before hitting the ground.

The tunneling was on a comparable level of sophistication. Grampa Stewart sometimes visited the shaft, but he never really worked at it except to make a few helpful suggestions about timbering. Most of the work was done by Art Hammond, Billy Bonnie, Jake, and me. Art's father, Old Man Hammond, usually did the cooking on those weekends. He was a crusty old man of very few words. If he had a real first name, nobody ever heard it. Old Man Hammond he was, and Old Man Hammond he stayed.

A weekend up Fall River was good for the soul. The aspens whispering, the gentle roar of the little creek called Fall River, the mountains towering over the cabin on both sides of the canyon — here was a peace I seldom found in Denver. I was a success. I liked the hustle and bustle of Denver and the twenties. But somehow there was always something special in the high country that I never felt anywhere else. Not that I worried about that for long. It was good to be young and alive, and soon time to get back to Denver and a busy life.

One Sunday afternoon when it was time to leave Fall River and head back to Denver, Art, Billy, Old Man Hammond, Conoco, and I started down Clear Creek Canyon. I was driving and was going pretty fast, sliding on some of the turns of the gravel road winding above the creek bed. We blew a tire and I fought to keep the car on the road, but I couldn't hold it. We hit the reflector pole, and for just an instant the pole seemed to hold. A moment later that last barrier gave way and we went over the edge, plunging thirty feet to the stream below. The car turned over in the air, doing a forward somersault and landing top down in the shallow creek bed. The impact smashed the doors open and spewed people in all directions.

I woke up in the Golden hospital. Billy had fished me out, still unconscious, from the pool where we landed. Old Man Hammond apparently had a broken arm, which he was refusing to have treated. Billy had a few bruises but wasn't too much the worse for wear. We were released from the hospital within an hour. I had a concussion. Billy turned out to have a wrenched knee and was cut some around the face. Old Man Hammond was still threatening to slug anyone who came near his broken arm. Muttering something about "drunks and fools," the emergency room doctor had finally given up and let us leave.

In the excitement we completely lost track of Art and Conoco. With the help of a passing trucker, Billy had managed to get me, Art's dad, and himself up the embankment and down to Golden. A couple of other cars had stopped at the accident and Billy thought Art and Conoco must be riding with them. Afterward at the hospital we finally realized that Art and Conoco had never arrived at the hospital.

We called Grampa Stewart in Denver and he came out to Golden to pick us up. We immediately drove back up Clear Creek Canyon to the point where we left the road. The car was a total loss and nobody was in sight.

"Let's go back to Golden and talk to the cops," Billy urged.

"And let's get a bottle while we're in Golden. I know a place," insisted Old Man Hammond.

When they arrived at the sheriff's office in Golden, a deputy ushered them to a cell where Art was sound asleep. "We found him on the far side of the stream after you left.

First we thought he was dead, but I think he was just so pie-eyed that he seemed dead. Probably what saved him. Say, how fast were you guys going anyway? And who was driving?"

The group suffered an attack of instant amnesia, but we did remember to explain that Art hadn't been drinking. As we remembered it, Art was receiving medication and was under a doctor's care.

Grampa introduced himself as Dr. Walter Black Stewart, and urged that "poor Mr. Hammond must be released at once in my care. I have no doubt that he must have been driving and simply blacked out after too large a dose of his medication."

The deputy grinned, "Well, you look sober, anyway . . . . Okay, get him out of here. But don't light any matches around that 'medication' of his."

On the way to Walt's car, the battered little group worked on reviving Art, who was still very much under the influence of his "medication." Art didn't have the vaguest idea of Conoco's whereabouts.

Old Man Hammond had an idea, the same idea he often had, "Now let's go get that bottle."

Problems with our growing mining business made it impossible to get back to Fall River for nearly two weeks. I didn't even make it up Clear Creek to retrieve the wrecked car until then. When I did get to the wreck, I looked everywhere in the rocks for Conoco, half afraid that I might find what I was looking for.

"Conoco's gone and that's for sure," I thought as I drove up Clear Creek Canyon on my way to Fall River. I was alone this time. Somehow I wanted to spend a weekend without anyone at the cabin. I'd been missing the dog and it was time to listen to the water, hear the wind in the trees, and think about old Conoco.

When I reached the cabin, I could hardly believe my

eyes. Conoco sat outside the cabin door, smiling that self-satisfied smile that especially wise dogs have when they're very pleased with themselves. The dog had apparently been thrown clear in the accident. With no way to follow me into a city of several hundred thousand people, Conoco had done the next best thing: he retraced the route to the cabin, over thirty miles from the accident in Clear Creek. He had arrived footsore and hungry and had waited patiently two long weeks for my return.

I guess dogs have more sense than people. Anyway, my old friend and I enjoyed that Fall River weekend.

Buffalo Bill

Pahaska ("the Long-Haired One"), the Indians called him. To everybody else, he was Buffalo Bill. Half the women of the world loved him, including types as different as Annie Oakley and Queen Victoria. Tall and handsome, a legend in his own time, Bill Cody was the remaining symbol of another age. The buffalo and the Indian had passed from the frontier, but Colorado still had Buffalo Bill. For some, he was the hard-drinking faker of the Buntline novels and the Wild West shows. For most, Bill was the victor in the fight to the death with Chief Yellow Hand at Warbonnet Creek, the authentic hero and gentleman, the soul of another time and place.

When the old scout finally passed from the scene in the twenties, he was buried on Lookout Mountain west of Denver. I wouldn't have been involved that day, but it happened that the bugler who was playing taps at the burial was an old friend of my family, Quince Record. At Quince's insistence, I went up Lookout Mountain that late spring day with Billy and Art, together with several thousand mourners and curiosity seekers. A semicarnival atmosphere prevailed. Onlookers drank whiskey straight from the bottle while oldtimers told lies about how well they had known Cody. The glass over Cody's face steamed over in the late afternoon sun. Out of the crowd came an obese old woman with the bearing of a queen. She stepped forward to the casket and shaded the casket glass with her parasol for the rest of the service. There was a strange dignity in that gesture. Bill Cody was being cared for and told goodbye one last time by one of those many ladies from back down the trail.

Quince Record played taps, and the crowd started back down the mountain as the sun dipped behind the hills to the west. "Somehow I think Cody was glad to go. This wasn't his world anymore." I wasn't so much speaking to anyone as just thinking out loud.

"Well, the old boy had quite a life," said Art.

"Yes," I mused, "and he had quite a time and place to live his life. I wonder if we have as much in our time."

No matter how busy things were, one place I could still be found was Grammaw Hagee's little house out on the Platte. It was a rare week that I didn't drive by to drop off a pork roast and stay on while Grammaw cooked dinner. The old lady was never too keen on automobiles but she never said no to a ride with her crazy grandson. In those days I usually had the fastest car in town. The Model T that I raced at Overland Park had magneto ignition, a "Rajah" head and double overhead valves. Tuned to perfection, that T would run 60 mph in low gear and couldn't be caught, especially on a mountain road. There were times on those drives in the mountains when Grammaw Hagee probably thought her hair was turning another shade whiter, but she never said a word about it to her favorite grandson.

The Sunday after Bill Cody was buried, Grammaw and I took stock of the world from that quiet front porch of the little house on the South Platte.

"Do you like what you're doing, George?"

"Sure, Grammaw."

"Do you want to do it for the rest of your life?"

"Gosh, Grammaw, I don't know. I suppose there are other things I'd like to try, but I'm enjoying what I'm doing."

"Well, then don't wait too long to try them, George. The world has a way of using up all our time if we let it. And there's a lot to learn and a lot of ways to feel about ourselves that we never discover unless we go after it."

"Grammaw, the mountains are sure pretty tonight, aren't they?"

"They're always pretty when we take the time to look, George. You should know that by now."

The small boy had grown up. The old pioneer woman had grown older, more stooped, but the love they shared for the mountains and for each other never wavered.

"Remember when we used to talk about the face of God, Grammaw?"

"Yes, George. Have you had any glimpses of His face lately?"

"Not as much as I used to. Maybe I've just been busy, but it seems that this spot, right here at twilight, is the only place where I ever feel that God is around close some-where."

"God's always close wherever you are, George. I told you long ago that the problem is in us, not in God. When we take time with our mind and heart, we can always find God. Maybe you've been too busy to take time." Conoco stirred at my feet and looked up at the sound of Grammaw Hagee's voice. He was a one-man dog, but he seemed to love those visits to the little house on the Platte almost as much as I did.

"Don't ever get too busy to look for God, George."

Time for a Change

Not all the ballyhoo of the 1920s was located in Denver. The lunacy had spread to other places as well, including the Gulch where our Mary Murphy was located. The Big Hotel where I stayed with Grampa Stewart on my first visit to the Gulch was back in operation. The hotel manager, a woman named Bernadette Cole, set the tone for the place. As she described herself, she had married three times, once for the sake of art (Mr. Morton, a dancing teacher), once for a child (Mr. Benedict, a fine athlete and former Olympic swimmer), and once for love (Mr. Cole, her current husband). The real excitement lay in the fact that all three husbands lived simultaneously at the Big Hotel, helping Mrs. Cole manage the place. They and a few other friends used to take outings together as a group. I've often thought that Mrs. Cole missed her calling. She had a great future as a marriage counselor.

One of Mrs. Cole's eccentric friends who lived several miles farther up the Gulch was a lady named Byrd Fuqua, given to large diamond rings, monkey-fur coats, cowboy hats, and collections of exotic bric-a-brac. One of her favorites that Grampa and I saw once when we visited the Gulch was Byrd's collection of shrunken heads. Byrd had the heads down at the Big Hotel, arrayed along a shelf and complete with a long and dubious story about how she had picked them up on the Amazon River. Grampa insisted that such things shouldn't be seen on an empty stomach. I agreed, and we adjourned to the hotel bar. After a calming drink or two, I asked Byrd how the heads could ever be made so tiny. She answered, "One way is to attend college. The other way is a long and complicated process of treatment used by the headhunters. Either way, you wind up with a perfect specimen for the museum case or for politics."

Byrd always liked to talk about her husbands too, especially one who had been picked up by a tornado and whirled three miles through the air where he knocked down a forty-foot tree. As Byrd said, "It takes a hell of a man to do that. I was really proud of Jack. It's a damn shame he didn't survive his triumph."

Not everybody in the Gulch was as crazy as Bernadette Cole or Byrd Fuqua. Most were the miners and ranchers and mountain people whose way of life had changed very little in the last fifty years. But somehow the lunatic fringe was coming a little closer all the time.

Our trips back to the Gulch came up fairly often, because we were operating the Mary Murphy. Usually Jake, Art Hammond, Billy Bonnie, and some of the rest would come along for the ride and we'd spend a few days working our way around the bars in Buena Vista and Salida, usually reserving at least one day for a stop at some of the old haunts in Leadville. For most of us, the trips were a combination of business and pleasure, but they were a special necessity for Art Hammond, who seemed always to have a sour business deal that required his temporary departure from town. Art had a tendency to pawn his tomorrows and completely forget his yesterdays, but he did live in a glorious present. He dreamed endlessly about the big take, the great success, which was just around the corner. If he had money, his friends were all welcome to it. And he tended to bounce back and forth between considerable sums of money and total poverty.

Art was willing to bet on anything and always had a few deals that were "absolutely sure-fire." My dog Conoco was one of his real favorites in that regard. Conoco never looked for trouble. But in his travels with us, he sometimes found himself in the company of people who felt they had really tough dogs. I would try to warn them off, but for some people that just makes them insist all the more. At that point, Art could usually manage to get a bet down, because he knew something that nobody else in the house could guess.

Conoco, that little wire-haired terrier, for all of his lack of size, had a way of fighting that almost always guaranteed a win. When a bigger dog charged him, he would seem to roll over on his back, allowing the charge to carry him over. But as the other dog bore down on him, Conoco would roll to the side. Suddenly the other dog's muzzle would be inside Conoco's mouth. At that point, it was all over. Either the other dog and the other owner backed off immediately, or Conoco would crunch down hard and send the teeth of the opposing dog flying in all directions. That almost never happened, because people were so surprised and the other dog so cowed that they were happy to let the whole thing go. At that point, Conoco would quickly back off and we would go back to being left alone.

Once when we finished one of these demonstrations that size doesn't always guarantee victory, the owner of the police dog turned to Art and, paying the twenty-dollar bet he'd just lost, mumbled, "I wish I owned half that dog." Art politely asked why and the thick-set, disgruntled loser said, " 'Cause I'd kill my half." Art took immediate offense and slugged him, with no apparent effect. By then Art knew he was in trouble and tried to back off, but he didn't move fast enough. The big man picked him up and threw him into the bottles behind the bar. Jake stepped in and flattened the tough guy, but it was a little late to save Art, who by then looked and smelled like the last rose of summer. He had enough whiskey and broken glass in his clothes to make him move very, very carefully. After that night in Buena Vista, Art thought it probably would be safer to go back to Denver again.

On the way back to Denver we found Art some fresh clothes. He perked right up. Jake was driving and Grampa Stewart was with him in the front seat of the Packard Twin Six we had then. Art, Billy, and I were in the back. Denver was about a hundred miles away through the mountains. We had stopped a time or two along the way and had emerged from each saloon to face a steadily graying, forbidding sky. The mountains were obviously getting ready to drop a heavy snowfall. The storm had begun before we reached Denver — heavy, sticky late spring snow bringing everything to a standstill. The last few miles down Turkey Creek Canyon and into Denver were more and more treacherous. We decided to go straight downtown and have dinner. By the time we had parked about a block from the Navarre, things were so bad that traffic had completely stopped. There was no sign of the storm stopping, so we decided to make a night of it at the Navarre until things cleared up. After wading through the snow, we discovered that the Navarre had decided not to open at all in the face of the storm, so we waded back through the snow and turned down Eighteenth Street for several blocks to a saloon we were sure would be open. Most of the stuff served there was a mixture of wood alcohol, snuff, and coffin varnish, but at least it was a place to get in off the street and away from a howling blizzard.

The bootleg whiskey was worse than we thought. The first drink or two felt as if I had swallowed a lighted kerosene lamp. After that, it didn't seem to make much difference.

We followed the weather reports as the evening wore on and it was obvious by midnight that we were in for one of the great paralyzing snowstorms of the century. The radio reported trains stranded on the continental divide, street signs and billboards collapsing, and growing general chaos. By then our intrepid little band and the few other customers trapped in the place were congratulating one another for our farsighted decision to keep out of the storm.

The telephone lines and the power lines were the next to go. Fortunately, the proprietor had some candles and kerosene lamps, plenty of whiskey and no intention of closing. There was so much snow piled up outside the door that we couldn't have pushed the door open to leave had we wanted to. As I look back on it, I wouldn't have missed that night for anything. Grampa Stewart began to think of all that snow and its paralyzing effect on modern, mechanized society. He started to wax philosophic: "So accustomed are all these people to their civilized toys that they think they're some kind of Robinson Crusoe if the power goes off." Grampa could sometimes betray a bitterness when he mixed drinking with philosophizing. Tonight was no exception. One of the other customers, warming to what Grampa said about modern society and its inability to face Nature, came around to Grampa's end of the bar and said, "I'm glad to know you."

To which Grampa Stewart replied, "Is that remark a sample of your brilliance?" That slowed the conversation a little.

Grampa tossed off a glass of whiskey. "All we get here is real rotgut. This town's been dry ever since Billy Sunday paid us a visit. Nowadays most of this slop comes down from Cheyenne. I hear they bring it down in hearses. Symbolic, don't you think? Anyway, back to the point. I wouldn't want you to think that I'm not in favor of modern technology. On the contrary, it has some unique advantages. We hear a lot these days about electrified houses. I think the possibilities there are endless. How about fixing up a nice comfortable electric chair? That way when people came to your house you could wave them to the chair with a special earnestness and get them all comfortable and then press the switch with a sigh of relief. I've been reading all those ads about the electrified houses and I haven't seen any reference to that possibility so far. I think we might be able to make a fortune there, George. Anyway, it doesn't make much difference; I see better with kerosene light. It's nice to have it darker. You can't see your watch so easily.

"The world right now is full of slaves who see their watch so clearly that they're tied down with the heaviest fetters imaginable, the watch chain. It's no wonder that most of our literature has for its main theme the story of lost people in a lost world. Civilization seems to be scaring the hell out of everybody. You can see it in the linoleum-makers' taste that we put into designing our buildings. You can hear its final death rattle in the miserable noise that passes for music.

"I think it's about time we got out of town, George, and got out of town to stay. We ought to get back in the hills where the country sings to us. The only place out here in the big towns where people are still singing is in some of the churches. It seems to me that people are haunted and one way or another they have to flee into sanctuary if they're going to continue to be able to sing."

It was a long night and there was a great deal more talk in the same vein. But that trip back from the Big Hotel and that crippling snowstorm of April 1929 set the tone for what was about to happen. The next few months would bring big changes for all of us. And all this came at a good time for me. Looking back on it now I can see that I was drifting. My careless living was catching up with me and, as Grammaw Hagee used to say, I had to decide what I was going to do and get on with it.

In one way this was decided for all of us with the crash in the fall of '29. We had a telegram from one of our New York partners to whom we had gone for capital in a large mining expansion that we had undertaken a few years before. It was a simple telegram: "The world has gone crazy. Close all operations at once." We went to work to save what we could and set about shutting down everything we could reach. We lost many of the properties in the process, but we did manage to pull enough together to save the Mary Murphy and a few other silver properties. We had no income, but we did have the basic properties if the mining industry and the economy ever came back. We had a bad ninety days while we were doing it, but we saved a lot. As we tightened up our holdings, it became more and more clear that Grammaw Hagee had been right — I had been drifting.

Grampa Stewart had also been right. There were some things deeply wrong with the modern world. Things he had said the night of the big snowstorm and on all those other nights I kept hearing. Grampa Stewart was a tough social critic, but he was no revolutionary. He thought that revolutionaries usually have nothing to revolt about and are themselves pretty revolting. But he also didn't have many kind words for the booster mentality that dominated the twenties. He loved to quote H. L. Mencken, "When a gang of real estate agents, bond salesmen, and automobile dealers gets together to sob for Service, it takes no Freudian to surmise that someone is about to be swindled."

"And who was swindled?" Grampa would ask. "Women who had been convinced that virtue was superfluous. Men who had so many time-saving devices that there was no time left for reflection. People who were so fascinated with the 'good life' that they forgot how to live at all.

"And all this wonderful new way to live has been put together for us in books explaining 'success.' Boosterism has brought a library shelf of books to show us how to succeed in everything, written by people who can't even succeed in writing a good book. Nobody would dare to publish a book about farming if he had never once been able to grow a single carrot. But the last few years have given us all kinds of books on 'success,' with absolutely no idea of what 'success' is or how to achieve it. Not that some people don't make a lot of money. A few months ago, just before the crash, George Baker's stock at the New York National Bank went up with a paper profit increase of $7.5 million in ten days. I guess that goes to show what hard work will do for a man. But damn it, George, these big paper profits and these big outfits totally out of touch with the work they're supposed to be doing aren't what this country is about. I'm for the business community and especially what we've done in mining. Entrepreneurs are fine — they make the world go. The real trouble is when the bigness gets as bad in business as it is in government. We then are at the point where the whole damn thing just won't work anymore.

"For me, George, I've about had enough. I've seen my fill of flashy men and women with hard eyes who don't respect one another and who don't respect themselves — people whose sole satisfaction lies in their capacity to impress one another. They're so sophisticated. They're so world weary. They're so wise, that they finally believe in nothing and in no one. They've been everywhere, they've done everything, and they've hated every damn boring minute of it. All that's left for them is to impress their fellow promoters. I've lived in that world. In the process I've seen beauty destroyed because it's 'uneconomic.' I've seen loyalty and love denied because they didn't 'pay.'

"George, the price that a world like that demands is too high — it's time I went home. And I hope you want to come with me. The hell with what we've lost. Let's go back up and run the Mary Murphy as small as we need to, maybe with just the two of us doing the work by hand. But let's get back in touch with something real."

The Little House on the Platte

When I first learned that Grammaw Hagee was seriously ill, I couldn't believe it. She had ever been the tough old lady who took care of everybody else and got on without complaining. But apparently she had been giving so much of herself away for so long that she had nothing left to give. Her old body was just about worn out when I visited her the last time in the little house on the South Platte. The doctor wanted to move her to the hospital, but she told him she'd lived in that house most of her life and that it would be good enough for her to die in.

"Well, at least let me give you a hypodermic. It will lessen your pain and make you much more comfortable."

"No thanks, doctor. If I'm going to meet my Maker, the least I can do is meet Him with a clear head."

Grammaw Hagee sat up in bed and I sat beside her, holding her hand as we looked out the window at the mountains and watched the twilight descend.

"The face of God is still out there, George. Don't wait any longer to look for it."

There were other people in and out that night and Grammaw Hagee and I didn't talk much more. She was gone before morning.

Sometimes in a moment of death, the loved one who is gone seems to be especially near. That was true of Grammaw. Her force of personality and her love were so strong that I knew she would always be with me. She understood that we have to be conscious of our own part in life, however modest, to be genuinely happy. Only then can we live in peace and die in peace. That sense of meaning finally gives the point to life and death. It was something that Grammaw Hagee understood very well.

That winter day in 1930 made the final decision complete. Everything Grampa Stewart had been saying, everything Grammaw Hagee had said for years, somehow came home to me. It was time to go back to the hills. As I did, Grammaw Hagee's voice was with me once again as the old woman and the boy sat on the porch of that little house on the South Platte and watched the sun go down behind the mountains.

"Grammaw, what do you think about when you look off in the distance and don't talk?"

"Old people look off in the distance to remember things which won't come again."

VI
THE ONLY THING WE HAVE TO FEAR ...

Grampa and I were back in the Gulch by summer 1930. We had been fighting to save as many of the properties as we could, but as the aftermath of the crash deepened all around us, the mining business came to an absolute standstill. We had borrowed too much money and were, plainly, stretched too thin. Property after property was getting away from us. We had enough cash to save the Mary Murphy and a few other mines free and clear and that was about all that was left of the mining empire.

Somehow, though, I just didn't care much. It was good to be home again, back up the Gulch. The Mary Murphy was entirely closed down. The crew had been given its last paycheck. Grampa and I moved back into the old cabin and spent the next several weeks boarding things up at the mine. Before long, I found the rhythms of my life slowing down to a more normal pace. The summer days were beautiful in the high mountains. The view high over the valley from the Mary Murphy was as spectacular as always. There wasn't a soul for miles and you could hear the wind rustling the leaves in the aspen trees. The long summer evenings back at the cabin found Grampa and me with a drink or two, a simple meal, and time to sit in front of the cabin and watch the mountains grow dark.

We had enough cash to take care of any needs that were likely to arise. We visited old drinking buddies when it was time to go to town for supplies. And we had that beautiful Gulch. The time in solitude to think and talk was perhaps the best of all. Grampa Stewart was getting pretty old. He'd always been something of a homespun philosopher, but in all the years I'd known him he usually had been pretty cynical and flippant about life. Somehow his advancing years and that special solitude at the cabin brought out a deeper, more thoughtful side. Over the next couple of years we did more reading and talking — real talking — than either of us had done in all the years I'd known him.

The thirties wore on, but the mining business remained dead. We couldn't begin to open the Mary Murphy and we got so we weren't sure we wanted to. The trips to town, the long talks, and that magnificent Gulch were what we really needed. Denver and the twenties and the big world all seemed far away.

As the decade wore on and the New Deal came to Washington, Franklin Roosevelt found one of his most dedicated critics in Grampa Stewart. For him, the political events of the thirties were an unfortunate continuation of a trend which he felt was already well advanced in America. For him, the whole world was growing too big and leaving too little room for regular people. There were too many rules and regulations, too many "experts," too little room to move. I remember so many of those conversations as we drove to Buena Vista for an evening at the Green Parrot and a fresh load of supplies, or as we sat outside the cabin and watched the mountains.

"The world is freezing into an ice age of conformity, George. Judging from the last twenty years, there's not much I can do about it, and not much you can do about it, either. But we can fight a delaying action, hold 'em off as long as possible.

"The trouble with the New Deal is that the pace seems to be picking up. It's harder and harder to fight that rear-guard action. The New Deal's no reform movement. It's a real revolution. The object isn't to work with our country as we know it; it's a deliberate attempt to change whatever's left of the country. Worse yet, it's not an honest shooting revolution. These bastards are going to do it with book-keeping and lawmaking.

"What really bothers me about these sons of bitches is their monstrous itch for changing people. I never saw so many evangelists and missionaries and PR hacks, all bent on reshaping and standardizing everybody according to their own disgusting ideas of how people should live. The vegetarians and the Prohibitionists and the socialists all have one thing in common. Everything they do is terrible even to think about.

"All the PR business types and the self-styled mission-aries are bad enough, but nobody can hold a candle to the political version of that itch to run everybody's business. Still, you have to have a certain admiration for those pol-iticians. If you can't respect 'em for their virtue, at least we ought to respect 'em for their professional capacities. I've known quacks of all sorts over the years, economic, judicial, theological, literary, and professorial, and none of them hold a candle to the political quacks. I remember reading somewhere not long ago that of the forty-eight governors now in office, four are presently under indictment by grand juries, one is in jail, seven are active members of the Ku Klux Klan, three are unreformed labor leaders, two are dipsomaniacs, five are bogus war heroes, and one is an astrologer. I believe H. L. Mencken wrote that somewhere, and he was just talking about the governors of the states. The real quackery is in Washington, D.C.

"Of all those political quacks in Washington, the social planner is the worst. We live in an age of self-styled experts, people who know so much about some one thing that they lose their common sense, if they ever had any. It seems that the more and more they butt into everybody's business, the less they understand what individual human beings are all about. They just can't believe that real people are out there running their own lives. I was reading somewhere about a Public Works Administration grant that was pushed off on the Amish down in Pennsylvania. The Amish not only didn't take the money, but appealed to the courts to have the whole deal scrapped. The interesting part was what happened next. At the PWA, fifteen of the bureaucrats fainted when the news arrived, eleven more went into convulsions, and three died. Unfortunately, this leaves several million to go.

"Somehow the idea got around that human nature is fine just the way it is and is likely to keep getting better and better. That's what's the matter with the twentieth century. It seems the farther we go down that self-deluding road, the more unhappy and more regimented the world gets. That modern planning equation that believes so much in 'technology' and 'progress' doesn't leave any room for the one important fact in our existence: God. When we quit trying to know God, we get trapped in the shallows of life. We're at the mercy of all that collective planning nonsense closing in on us.

"I've been kicking around for damn near eighty years, George, and a lot of that time has been a fool's errand. But no matter how bad things get in this world, the wind still comes from the mountain tops, the clouds still gather in the sky, the snow still comes down, and the country is still here all around us. It's real, it's untouched, and God is here for anyone who bothers to see.

"If we do ever manage to get life back on a human scale, that saving job will be done here in the West, in America, and it'll be done by Americans. And when we do it, we'd better remember it's a job we'll have to do alone — not with some damn committee. There are some things you can't give to somebody else, some things that have to be earned. You even have to be careful giving too much to people you love. It's so easy to give that you finally give away everything — courage, kindness, sharing, earning, even the pleasure of giving itself. We all need a reason to be. We need to know who we are, why we're doing the job. If you take that from your loved ones, or your friends, or even from complete strangers, you're being selfish. You get so busy enjoying giving that you don't see what you're doing to the people on the receiving end. You have to give them a chance too, if you really love them. Give 'em a chance to earn, to give from what they've earned. Give 'em the respect they deserve.

"Some things in this life have to be done alone. The trouble with that divine spark is that it is so elusive. It's so easy to try to put it in a concrete form — a political system, a social institution, a church. Every time we try to catch the kingdom of heaven and put it in a bottle, every time we give it a temporal shape, we're asking for trouble. People who seek that divine spark on their own will find it together. The misguided attempt to reach that divine spark as part of a collective mob always destroys the spark and finally destroys the mob.

"The only thing that really makes sense is loving somebody, doing your job, taking what life gives without running away. We don't really do that alone. We do it with one another and we do it with God. And that's the beauty of this country, when we give it a chance to work. You'll never be closer to it than when you're looking out at those mountains here in this Gulch. Now hurry up and get to town. I want a drink before dinner."

Jodie

I'd known Jodie off and on since she was a little kid. Her father Jack Cogan ran one of the big ranches out in the valley. He was already an old man in the thirties and had homesteaded the place before the turn of the century. Jack was head of the clan, a tough Irish family that produced strong sons in every generation to carry on the place. The Cogan ranch was beautiful bottom land on the Arkansas with rich meadows along the river, extending up the several creeks that ran through the Cogan place on their way to the main stream. Whiteface cattle, hard work, Democratic politics, and the Roman Catholic church were all the Cogans needed. They were on their land with their family and they liked it that way.

I watched Jodie grow up around her daddy Jack, her Uncle Bill, and all the brothers. Jodie was by far the youngest of Jack's children and was the apple of his eye. Anyone who came around that house with an eye for Jodie had better make damn sure his intentions were in good order. I had been around there for years, more as a drinking buddy of Jack, Bill, and the sons. But when we returned to the Gulch in the thirties, for the first time I noticed that Jodie was a great deal more than a snotty-nosed ranch kid.

She had grown up when I wasn't looking. I suppose this first struck me about 1935. We had been doing some assessment work at the mine and were keeping the property maintained against the day when we thought prices would revive and we would reopen the Mary Murphy. My life was a happy one, and I did have more than enough time to go to town when I wanted and stop by the Cogan ranch on the way home. It was about that time that Jodie's Uncle Bill was killed. Walt and I were in Buena Vista that day and only a few hundred feet from the railroad tracks, down by the Green Parrot, when it happened. The freight train was heading south from Leadville, down the long grade. Bill had been driving his old Model T truck across the tracks in the middle of town when he killed the engine right on the tracks. He tried a few times to start it and couldn't. By then he was aware of the train coming down from the north. That truck couldn't have been worth $75, but Bill wasn't about to give up on it. He got out and tried to push it off the tracks. By then, some of us were running toward the crossing. But we had too far to go. The train was bearing down, and instead of jumping back, Bill got in that damn old truck and tried again to start it. He and the truck were carried on the front of the train for hundreds of feet down the track. I think he never knew what hit him.

What possesses a man to risk and lose his life for some worthless thing? That's something I guess none of us will ever understand. I know that Bill Cogan worked hard all his life. Probably the tough old man was determined that nothing, not even a railroad train, was going to take something that belonged to him. Whatever the reason for his death, Bill's funeral was a good one. The Cogans had friends up and down the Arkansas Valley and we were all there. The little Catholic church in Buena Vista was filled to overflowing. Jodie's Uncle Bill was the first person close to her she had lost, but she took it really well. That sandy hair and those big blue eyes and that strong chin all reflected dignity. I believe that's when I really saw her for the first time as a woman.

After that she began to be included in some of the things we did. The first time Jodie and I ever really went out together as a couple happened when Bill Wisecarver and his new wife came up from Denver. The four of us drove over to Minturn on the far side of Battle Mountain and had a picnic in a high mountain valley. We ate steaks cooked on willow branches over an open fire and ate beans from the can with the same branches, since somebody had managed to forget the silverware. The train from Minturn grinds up a long grade toward Battle Mountain and there is a stretch where the cars are moving very slowly. That gave Bill and me a chance to hop a few freights and ride them to the point where the train reached the downgrade and started to pick up speed. We would ride as long as we dared, roll off, and walk back down the valley, have another drink, hop another freight — a good afternoon in a high meadow filled with wildflowers and a cool breeze off the mountains.

Bill told me about his regular job in Denver. Mabel had decided it was time for him to settle down. He was working at a Remington arms plant west of Denver. The main trouble he seemed to have was that the guards at the plant weren't used to people who drank on the job. A mechanic on a cold concrete floor, Bill had been doing that all his life and he didn't like stopping. He did manage to cut down to the point where he did his drinking *before* he came to the plant. Even then they gave him trouble. It wasn't that Bill was drunk. His drinking never seemed to interfere with his work. It was just one of those rules at the plant.

In fact, it reached the point where the guard would see Bill drive up to the gate, automatically motion for him to roll down the window, and ask him to exhale. Bill got sent home twice because of the heavy blast of alcohol that hit the guard in the face. Bill had the last laugh. As we sat by the fire in that meadow above Minturn, Bill told Jodie and me about the day he had gone home before work and eaten a handful of garlic cloves plus a couple of onions. That load, on top of the normal cargo of alcohol and Copenhagen on his breath, produced quite an effect when the guard asked him to roll down the window and Bill blew in his face. The guard turned white, waved him on, and never asked him to stop again.

Bill seemed happy enough at the time. But looking back on it I supposed I should have seen that there was something in Mabel that would change the kind of rough life that the tough old German was used to. It was hard for Bill to be a family man and hold down a regular job. He was better off with the boys and at his best working all night to get a car running in time for the main event the next day.

Anyway it was a wonderful day for Jodie and me and the beginning of a series of wonderful days. She loved Grampa Stewart and would often come up and spend a day at the Mary Murphy with us. I was always welcome in the Cogan home and spent a lot of time with old Jack and the brothers, sitting at that kitchen table and having a drink or two before we sat down to one of the huge meals those ranchers managed to shovel away. Jodie never seemed to mind. She was so much a part of that independent ranch environment herself that she always understood. I didn't realize for a long while how much I loved her.

One of Jodie's favorite spots was a few miles down the Arkansas near Salida. One late May afternoon, she took me to Adobe Park, a pinon-covered stretch of ranch land overlooking the Arkansas Valley. We drove a few miles into the hills and stopped beside a tiny creek in a high meadow. At that point we could look directly up the face of Mt. Shavano, towering above us with the last melting snow still clinging to the sides of the mountain.

"I brought you here to see something you can only see at this time of year — and you can see it best from this spot," Jodie told me as we stood looking up at Shavano.

The winter's snow was melting, leaving only the ice and snow caught in the deep ravines on the face of the mountain. The last snows formed a great wingspread white angel, dominating the mountain and appearing to hang in the air above us. I'd seen the formation from the road before, but never as it appeared from this meadow at the foot of the mountain itself. The angel of Shavano glistened about us, surrounded by the majesty of the mountain and crowned by one of those deep-blue Rocky Mountain spring skies.

Jodie stood there, looking up the hill. "Shavano was a Ute war chief who had a good friend in the cavalry, a black scout named Jim Beckworth. I don't know how a Ute war chief and an army scout got to be friends, but they did. Beckworth was killed in a fall from a horse in 1851. The story is that Shavano came here to pray for the repose of the soul of his friend. The next spring, according to the legend, the angel appeared for the first time, giving promise that the prayer had been answered, that all was right with the world, and that renewal and rebirth were coming again with the spring. The old angel's been up there every spring since.

"For me, that legend says that cowboys and Indians — and all the rest of us — can count on God keeping His promises. Spring does come every year."

I can still see Jodie standing there, looking up at the angel. She was right — God's promises are kept.

Private Property

It was in the late thirties that Jack Cogan did something that brought a lot of pleasure to Grampa Stewart's last years. One of the major New Deal decisions in the thirties was whether to build a big water reclamation project connecting the western and eastern slopes of the Rockies. One of the places under consideration for the project was the Upper Arkansas Valley.

We hadn't heard too much about the whole thing until the day that Ed Gregg and the *Chaffee County Republican* reported that we were about to be visited by no less than the secretary of the interior. He and various Washington and Colorado dignitaries planned to come in person to inspect the new sites. An entourage like that attracts a whole caravan of automobiles and bureaucrats. Neither Grampa nor I was there when it happened, but we heard the same story enough times to believe it. The ribbon-cutters and photographers and state bureaucrats and federal bureaucrats were all hovering around Mr. Ickes as the entire party walked on a little farther from the last point that the caravan of automobiles could reach. They were nearing the headwaters of a creek flowing east out of the mountains and down toward the Arkansas in an area where they thought the east-west connection might be made. As they came across the meadow and crested a little hill, who should be sauntering up from the creek bed with his irrigation boots on but old Jack Cogan — with a red face and a great shock of snow-white unruly hair. The first person in the secretary's party apparently thought that Jack was sullying the ceremonial dignity of the moment, since he was the only one there without a suit. He asked Jack who he was.

"I'm Jack Cogan and you're on my land. Who the hell are you?"

In a patronizing, soothing tone, Jack was told to hold his voice down because this was the secretary of the interior, Harold Ickes, and his group, and they had come to discuss an important reclamation project.

Jack answered, this time in a louder voice, "This is my land. You're trespassing. Get off or I'll run you off."

"But you don't understand . . . "

"You're the one that doesn't understand. Get the hell off and get off now."

The United States government, the state of Colorado, and the press took one look at Jack and did just that. I suppose it couldn't happen now, but Grampa Stewart and I were both glad to be living in a country where it could still happen.

What Is This Thing That Comes to Me?

My old wire-haired terrier had been with us for years by the midthirties. He and Grampa Stewart had grown old together. Conoco had whipped just about every dog that had been foolish enough to challenge him and I suppose that's what finally got him in trouble.

Jodie and I were in Buena Vista one day in the fall of 1936. We were in the hardware store and Conoco was on his own out by the truck. By then he was old and stiff and beginning to get a little frail. A big chow almost twice his size, whom Conoco had whipped in a fair fight a few years before, came along the street while we were inside. He challenged old Con. Con got slowly to his feet. The old wire-haired terrier just didn't have sense enough to know he shouldn't fight. They went at it. Of course, Conoco got the worst of it. The chow was too big and Con was too old, but the old toughie just couldn't give up.

It was just then that I came out of the side door of the hardware store. I had on a heavy pair of hobnailed miner's boots and timed my three strides forward so that I could get a good, square kick under the chow's chest. I got him good and he went completely up into the air, over backward and landed in a heap. His owner was across the street at the Buena Vista Hotel. He had been watching the fight and thought it all pretty funny. But what had just happened to his dog he thought not so funny and he came charging across the street.

"What the hell did you do to my dog?"

I was holding Con in my arms, cut and bleeding, his old chest heaving. Jodie stepped between us with her eyes blazing and said, "You'd better get away from here while you still can, mister." There was something in her, and in the way she held those little shoulders, that made her meaning clear. The rancher looked at me, looked at Jodie, looked at his dog — and retreated to the hotel. Conoco had won his last fight, or at least he didn't back away from it.

Somehow everyone, including Con, seemed to know his time was due. That evening back at the cabin, Jodie and I patched him up as well as we could. He was gracious and appreciated the attention. When we were finished, he shambled right past the food we put out for him and lay down in a corner to take a sleep. He was there with us that evening, like always, but he didn't get up in the morning. Another of my tough old friends was gone.

· A few months later, death paid us another visit. Grampa Stewart's health had been getting steadily worse for the past year or two. A man who had spent most of his life in the mines, he had a bad case of silicosis. Years of breathing the dust below ground had gradually formed chunks of rock in his chest. The largest of these was the size of a cherry, the smallest the size of a cherry pit. Some of the coughing spells forced bloody bits of that rock from his chest and racked the body of that tall, lanky old Scotsman until it seemed he couldn't stand another siege.

Grampa always kept this pretty much to himself. He would usually toss off a drink or two, take a deep breath, and then get on with whatever he had been doing. Still, the face became more ashen, the chest more sunken, the back more hunched.

You would never guess it when the old boy went to town, though. He would stand a round or two of drinks, although he usually had that big cigar unlighted now.

He had a great heart, physical as well as symbolic. He slugged it out with death toe to toe. I watched him be so perversely proud that he encouraged people to think he was drunk when actually he was seriously ill.

Privately, with a wink, he would tell me, "Other people are always busy talkin' about dying. By God, I'm doing it!"

The day had to come. It did come, at the cabin where I believe Grampa would most have wanted to be. It was dusk and the long twilight was gradually veiling the mountains from our view inside the little cabin. This man who had been talking all his life, philosophizing about God and His world and everything in it, had no great deathbed speeches. He reached out his paper-thin, yellowed hand to me and said, "What is this thing that comes to me?"

I don't believe Grampa Stewart belonged in this century. He never handled all the bigness and the regimentation — all the bullshit. He never really believed that somehow big business or big government or big labor or big whoever could do more about his life than he and his friends could on their own.

I would miss him. I would never have another opportunity to gather the strength and courage from him that he had in such large quantities to fight the battles. He usually felt those battles were already lost before they were fought. But he was a man from another time and another place. He couldn't ever give up.

I suppose all of us carry within us our memory of a special golden age. We always want to push the values and attitudes of our golden age on younger people who are still forging theirs. Perhaps that's why old men should not be permitted pens and clocks and calendars. Still, I don't think a man is really old until regrets take the place of dreams. For Grampa Stewart, the dream was always there, just over the next hill. It was all around him in those beloved mountains.

I believe Jodie had come to love Grampa Stewart in her own way almost as much as I loved him. We spent all our time together after Grampa Stewart's death and were married before the end of 1937. The Cogans put on a wedding that everybody in the Upper Arkansas would remember. We were married in that little Catholic church in Buena Vista and had a wedding reception that stretched from the Green Parrot to the Cogan ranch. Neither of us could think of any other place on the face of the earth where we could be more alone than at the old cabin. So we went straight there to honeymoon and to set up housekeeping. The trip up the Gulch was beautiful that night. The moon was out, giving an eerie light to the ridges of the mountains and the deep shadows of the forests below. The air was fresh and clean. The Cogans had made a real effort to get me too drunk to move, but somehow tonight I could have drunk anything and still kept my wits. That night at the cabin I was home with the past and future, with the ghosts and my bride. We all loved one another and somehow it seemed that everything would be all right with the world.

Mining was picking up a little by 1937. We couldn't run a full operation, but we could work several men and operate in a marginal way while we gradually expanded and renovated for the resurgence of mining which we were sure was going to come. Jodie pitched in with me in the mine and gave me several of the happiest years of my life in that little cabin. We continued to look out on the world together and to leave the Gulch only when we needed company. But we knew perfectly well that the really important part of both our lives was there in the Gulch with us all the time.

If I'd gone with her to Buena Vista that day in 1940, she and I would probably still be living in this cabin together. Somewhere down by her dad's ranch she was met head-on by a driver from Denver. He was passing on a curve. I think she never suffered. I think she never knew what hit her. My little Jodie was gone. I thought my last reason for being in the Gulch had gone with her.

Soon after that came the offer from the syndicate in New York to include the Mary Murphy in a large silver and lead project coming on line with the approaching war. I jumped at the chance, because I was ready to go anywhere to be away from my memories and away from the Gulch. I thought one life was ending and another was about to begin when I moved to New York.

I underestimated the real strength of the Gulch.

VII

WHO SAYS YOU CAN'T GO HOME AGAIN?

Twenty years hurried by in Washington and New York. I was busy and successful, and had a full taste of power, prosperity, and progress. I thought I had left the Gulch behind for good. I was wrong. I have already told you the story of my return in 1960. I found that the Gulch had not ceased to exist. It was still there waiting for me — the country and the memories.

It's true that by the eighties places like the Gulch had become nothing more than a few isolated enclaves of an older America which has been largely submerged in "progress." Still, the soul of that older America lingers — not just in the memories, but in the people themselves. I have

161

come to know a lot of those people since I came back here twenty years ago.

Some of the characters I got to know in the sixties and seventies *were* out of another time and place. Walt Fox was Buena Vista's town marshal. Tall, thick-set, with a broad, pockmarked face, Walt was a man of few words. At first glance you might look right past him, but there was something that would bring you up short — not a sense of menace exactly, more a feeling of power under restraint. Walt could walk into the Green Parrot in the midst of an argument that was about to turn into a fight, take a quiet seat in a corner of the bar, and you could *feel* the stillness start to spread around the room.

Walt Fox was a quiet man, a decent man, and a tough man. I'll never forget the night Walt rolled his pickup north of Buena Vista. He'd had the night off and was coming home from a Mexican place in Granite where he liked to eat. A couple miles outside town, he couldn't make a curve, drifted into the gravel on the edge of the road, lost control, and wound up in the ditch with the truck lying across his legs. It was cold, he was alone at night on a deserted mountain road, and he knew that he must either move or die.

Walt worked his broken legs out from under the truck, located the pitchforks stuck upright in the slot behind the cab, took a deep breath, and hoisted himself to his feet.

The pain in the broken legs was sharp, but Walt kept going down the road, braced on those pitchforks. The tines were stuck into the ground with each step, the weight of his body supported by the strength of his arms and hands as he grasped the handles of the pitchforks. He had gone over half a mile toward town, dragging his smashed legs behind him, when a trucker saw him and stopped.

In three months he was back on the job as town marshal. Walt never talked much about that night (or about anything else, for that matter). I guess he thought it was all part of the job.

Somehow I've always believed that so long as a few such uncomplicated souls are out there in our country, we can know that the frontier is never quite gone, and never will go.

Old Man Nachtrieb

Some of the natives were a good deal more colorful and a good deal less reliable. Old Man Nachtrieb was pushing eighty when I knew him. Father of a big brood of sons who ran several ranches, Nachtrieb was the Upper Arkansas' answer to Old Man Clanton. He spent his full time as a self-appointed social critic and a regular patron of the Green Parrot. He was a tough old bird, with a mean mouth and the florid complexion that only a half century of heavy drinking can produce. He often bragged that he could eat and drink anything, adding the afterthought that the strange antics of politicians were probably due to faulty digestion — or, as he put it, "flabby guts to match flabby heads."

On those rare occasions when one of his sons tried to keep the old man out of trouble, it was guaranteed he would turn to the bar, toss off a drink, run one hand through his tangled white beard, and announce to no one in particular, "Be careful, be careful — the world's so full of chicken shit that all it can do is be careful."

Being careful was never Old Man Nachtrieb's style. He was helping his sons roof a barn one day and had been hitting the bottle a little as the day wore on. They worked until it was getting too dark to see and the boys were ready to quit, but not the old man. He had to make one last trip up the ladder. He was straddling the roof peak and getting down one last row of shingles in the dark. As he finished

and turned to come down the steep pitch of the roof, he slipped off the ladder. His sons heard a scream and looked up to see the old man hanging by his beard which he'd nailed to the roof. The boys rescued him, but they never let him forget it.

Nachtrieb was a little like my Grampa Stewart in his suspicion toward the medical profession. He refused to wear glasses and refused even to visit an eye doctor, muttering something about "chainsaw ophthalmology." His favorite line on doctors was, "Doctors are useless above ground. They ought to be six feet under, helping the garden grow."

Once Old Man Nachtrieb was trucking a load of hay from one Nachtrieb ranch to another. The boys didn't like him out on his own at his age, but he was a hard man to stop. Nachtrieb stopped in town, got drunk, played five-card stud, and lost all his money plus the load of hay. On the way home he got sleepy and stopped his now empty truck to take a nap. He awoke a few hours later, got out and walked around the truck, took a deep breath to clear his head, and announced to the mountains towering over him, "If I'm Chuck Nachtrieb, I've lost a load of hay. If I'm *not* Chuck Nachtrieb, I've found a truck!"

Everybody around, including the long-suffering doctors, expected Old Man Nachtrieb to live forever. Like an old, gnarled pine tree clinging to the bank of Chalk Creek even though completely undercut by the erosion of the stream, the Old Man seemed timeless. But time was catching up with the old villain. He could still work all day when he decided to. He could drink with the best of 'em, which he usually decided to. But somewhere down inside was a nagging ache that was a little more insistent all the time. The Old Man paid no attention. He'd lived his life without begging off and saw no reason he should start now.

He was driving his pickup to town for Saturday morning

errands (and maybe a stop at the Green Parrot) when the little ache became a great stabbing pain.

The old pine tree finally lost its hold and toppled into the creek.

Elijah, the Wonder Horse

Bill and Al Turner had been running horses in the Saguache mountains for twenty years. A long, lanky pair of weathered cowboys, the brothers raised horses, wintered them in the high mountain valleys, and then put them out in strings for working ranches and dude ranches during the summer months. And then one winter something happened that got them on the national news.

It all started with a string of horses the Turners had in a high mountain valley up Cottonwood Canyon. The Turners knew that with enough hay available down close to the water in a relatively sheltered area, a few horses could winter nicely. The horses were about halfway through the winter when a plane load of skiers from Aspen detoured slightly south on Aspen Airways on their way back to Denver. A New York ad man and his party caught sight of one old cowpony standing alone in the snow out in this high mountain pasture. They didn't know why he was there and they didn't bother to ask after they got to Denver. Their sensibilities were aroused (but not enough to go to Buena Vista and find out what was going on). They *were* aroused enough on their flight from Denver to New York to plan a campaign to "save" that poor old horse. The ad man knew how to handle public sentiment. He picked a name and launched a campaign. Within a few days the whole country had heard about Elijah, the wonder horse. Money was collected, airlifts were organized. Before it was through, Elijah and his pasture mates in that mountain meadow had been bombarded by enough hay bales to be a real risk to their survival.

Now Elijah had never needed help in the first place. Nor had the other horses, nor had the Turner brothers. But nobody came to Buena Vista to check, at least not for a long time. When one reporter finally came up from Denver to get the real story on the airlifts to these poor starving horses, he quickly uncovered the real story, much to the amusement of the Turners and everybody else for fifty miles up and down the Arkansas Valley.

Since the Denver reporter's paper had been one of the airlift organizers and general drumbeaters for the whole extravaganza, the real story never got into the papers.

Everybody in Buena Vista knew. They and their horses had been getting by for a long time before the beautiful people in New York noticed they had a problem. They're still getting along.

Christmas Eve

I'd known Bill Wisecarver since the twenties. He was the best mechanic I ever knew. He also was the most bull-headed little kraut who ever lived. For him America was the greatest country in the world. A man was free to make his own mistakes, to be his own man. He was loyal to his adopted country and loyal to his friends. Loyal in fact to a fault — and usually in trouble.

Once in the late sixties when he was driving up from Denver to see me, he made it as far as the hotel in Fairplay where he proceeded to get into a good-sized brawl. He was alone and had to deal with the regulars in the Fairplay Hotel — all at once. By the time Bill arrived at the Green Parrot in Buena Vista, he was bleeding from the nose and mouth and had most of his teeth kicked in and a few ribs broken.

And what did the little monkey want to do about it?

"George, come on back with me. I got in over my head. There were too many of 'em and I need some help." I was getting too old for stuff like that, but four or five of us went back with Bill that night and helped him settle things in Fairplay.

I supposed Bill attracted loyalty because he gave it so freely. He always gave one hundred percent. I never quite knew for sure what he meant, but there was a certain stage in the evening when you could count on Bill to say, "Pull the hammers back, it's time to go down the hill."

We went down the hill together many, many times.

Over the years I didn't see as much of Bill as I once had. And then, about 1970, a few days after New Year's, I got word that Bill had picked up a part-time job delivering coal in Denver. He was delivering partial loads in a dump truck on Christmas Eve, taking an occasional nip from the bottle lying next to him on the front seat. Apparently, with the lift up and half a load still in the bed, the dump had jammed on a lump of coal. Bill reached back beneath the bed to free the jam and the load came down, crushing him from the waist up.

I wish I'd been around to tell him goodbye.

Equinox

Old friends go away, one way or another. New friends come along when you give them a chance. Not long after Bill's death I met an old sheepherder who was down from the hills. Vince Flanagan was one of those local characters who had been around for years. Gibby knew him well and introduced us one evening at the Green Parrot. We closed the place that night, with Vince spinning those yarns of his. You could never be sure just where the truth stopped and the tale started, but with Vince it seemed not to make much difference. His stories were the kind that ought to be true, whether they were or not.

Listening to that tall, broad old man with the mane of white hair and the huge walrus mustache, I would sense a touch with reality that most people seemed to lack. His dark eyes would look out at you from that deeply lined face with a message that might have come from another world. Vince had been a sheepherder as long as anybody around Buena Vista knew. But something about him made it clear there had been a lot more to his life. He never talked about it, but he was clearly an educated man. We knew him as a sheepherder, and a sheepherder he preferred to remain.

That first night at the Green Parrot Vince told a story I'll never forget, a story that told me something about the Gulch I had never known. Years before, he had been running sheep for the O'Connor family on one of the ranches out in the valley. It was late spring and time to take a flock up toward the high country. The second day's drive into the hills, Flanagan had been caught in one of those late spring snows — wet, heavy, blinding. He, his horse, and his border collie had settled down in a high meadow with the flock to wait out the storm. The storm didn't let up. Flanagan soon realized he was in trouble, for this was one of those freak snowstorms that turn the late spring meadows into impassable snow fields.

The fire hissed and sizzled as the large, wet flakes smothered the camp. The face of Mt. Princeton, which loomed above the meadow, vanished in the blinding white blanket filling the air. There was no hope of getting the sheep down the mountain, not much hope of Flanagan getting himself down the mountain. The dog, the horse, the sheep, and the man huddled closer and closer together with the instinctive knowledge that death was hovering in the air above them.

Flanagan knew he had to do something soon. The warm cocoon of falling snow was settling over the camp, sealing man and animals from all reality, all sight and sound. Suddenly the sheepherder remembered the mine shaft. Once, years before, he'd been up on Mt. Princeton and had noticed what looked like a small opening on the eastern face of the mountain, well above timberline. When he had clambered over the face of the slide rock and worked his way up to the opening, he discovered a mine shaft which was almost invisible from the valley floor, mute testimony to the optimism and courage of some miner in the 1880s who searched for his fortune high on the face of a wind-swept mountain.

The tunnel Flanagan found that day ran at an angle back into Mt. Princeton. The timbers were rotten, the mine abandoned for sixty years. Outside, a faint trail ran across the face of the mountain, marking the old path of the ore wagons on their way to and from the mine. Apparently no one had been up to the shaft in many years. The peculiar angle of the small opening made it almost invisible unless you were right on top of it.

The erosion running down the eastern face of Princeton intersected the faint old wagon road. On his way down the mountain at twilight that day years before, Flanagan had noticed that the shadows etched in the eastern face by the afterglow of the sun setting behind the mountain formed a cross, with the old mine shaft almost exactly at the center of the cross, where the road and the erosion met. He had been standing in a high meadow, looking up at the cross which loomed above him. He'd tried for years to see that cross again, with different locations and different times of day. But he'd never been able to discover it again, except in that high valley at twilight.

Now Flanagan was in that meadow again, dying in the snow with his dog, his horse, and a herd of sheep. As soon as he remembered the mine shaft, he knew what he had to do. The way to survive a mountain storm is to get down the mountain. But what if you can't get down the mountain? Why, go *up* the mountain, of course! If they could reach that tunnel, they might have a chance. Impossible! Nobody could get a herd of sheep above timberline in a blinding, suffocating snowstorm. The sheepherder probably couldn't find the tunnel to save himself, much less the sheep.

"Well, I'm sure as hell not going to wait here to die. Come on, dog, let's give it a try."

And so they started, Flanagan leading the horse to break a trail, the dog rousting the sheep into single file in the path left by the man and the horse. Except in that narrow trail, the snow was over the head of the dog and the sheep. Flanagan was struggling ahead in drifts to his waist. On they went, blinded by the snow, the man and the horse exhaling clouds of steam with their every exertion. On they went, struggling up the face of the mountain, floundering ahead a few feet, falling back in the snow, rising again to gasp for air and plunge on.

The sheep were struggling and frightened, wallowing in the ragged trail behind the horse. The dog plunged back and forth along the line of sheep, forcing them on, fighting to keep them up and moving.

"The real trouble was, I couldn't see a damn thing. The going was so tough that we couldn't make it much farther. The sheep kept trying to quit, but that dog wouldn't let 'em. I don't know how he did it. I don't know how that horse lasted, either. But he did. I couldn't see two feet and was falling down more than standing up. Somehow we found our way across the face of that mountain, above timberline in the wildest storm I ever saw. I'd been working my way along the cross and damn near fell in the mine shaft before I saw it. We got all the sheep in, didn't lose a one. The sheep were damn near dead, the dog and the horse were worse, and I could hardly stand up, but we were warm — and alive.

"I don't believe I found that shaft on my own. I believe I was meant to find it. That's why I discovered it by accident years ago. God has His own plans, you know.

"The wet sheep didn't smell too good that next day, but the dog, the horse, and I weren't anything to write home about, either. Spring snow in Colorado goes as fast as it comes. We were on our way back down the mountain in twenty-four hours. Never told the owners about it. They probably wouldn't have believed me anyway."

The Truth Shall Make You Free

After that first time at the Green Parrot, I saw quite a bit of Vincent Flanagan. He always had a story to tell and was somehow very much at peace with himself and his world.

The best way to see Flanagan and listen to those yarns was to visit him in camp when he had some sheep up in the mountain meadows. I visited him one summer when he was camped in that same meadow where he first saw the cross. Sure enough, as the sun went down behind the mountain, the shadows of the erosion and the mining road deepened into the very image he had described. ·

As we sat by the fire in the fresh grass, with the aspens rustling in the breeze, the mountain towering above us, and the valley spread out far below, a camp robber swooped down from the trees and scolded us for trespassing in his meadow. The same border collie Flanagan had with him in the vernal equinox was still on duty — so old and wise that he didn't have to do much more than give the sheep the evil eye to keep them in line.

We cooked on the open fire and washed dinner down

with a mixture of whiskey and coffee. As it grew dark, Flanagan started to talk. The old sheepherder never seemed to need much encouragement.

"You know, George, we're all afraid — afraid of different things, maybe, but still afraid. We cover that fear up in lots of ways. Everybody has a favorite: drink, pride, sex, work, arrogance, food — lots of ways. Sooner or later, though, that fear will get us, unless we lay it down once and for all. The question is how?

"People have been trying to come up with the answer to that question as long as there've been people. One of the nice things about being a sheepherder is, you have a lot of time to ask questions like that and think about the answers. I've also got a nice setting up here in the mountains to do my thinking and I've got good company to talk to, like my dog and that camp robber. And I've gradually managed to come up with a few of the answers. I'm not sure the world's ready for my answers. In fact, I'm pretty sure it's not. Too bad. I'll tell you, George, if I could get people to try my answer, they'd be so grateful that even the undertaker'd be sorry when I died."

Flanagan laid back on his saddle and blanket and looked up at the mantle of stars overhead in the summer sky. You never knew for sure when he was pulling your leg. What you could count on was that it wouldn't be long until he'd be answering his own questions, and usually his answers were worth hearing.

"All you have to do to get over that fear is *tell the truth*. Somebody said 'the truth shall make you free.' He was right. It's simple. That's all there is to it.

"Truth, if you place her in the very heart of your life, will give you everything you need. Then you can quit worrying about those things you can't handle and start living — smell the flowers, feel the sun, start living. The Bible already said it. If you mean what you say, if you really speak the truth, you're free.

"George, I've raised more hell than most people. It's a long story, and one I'm not going to tell, but I didn't used to be a sheepherder. I feared more than most and lost more, and told more lies — to the world and especially to myself. I finally found out that you can't really love or be loved until you love the truth. No truth, no love.

"And everything that doesn't turn to love sooner or later turns to hate. Being a tough guy won't get you through. Being a nice guy won't get you through. Sooner or later, we have to learn that God runs the world. We can decide to go along, or we can go to hell. The fact is, we're *all* in hell even in this life until we accept the truth.

"Once we do that, the truth is all around us, in all those places where we looked but never saw what was right before us. The whole earth is sacramental; what the churches call grace is everywhere we look.

"God knows, I'm no churchgoer. As near as I can make out, an awful lot of what they call 'religion' has more to do with men than with God. I always figured that God showed His Son first to a few shepherds because they were more in touch with the world than all the high priests in Jerusalem.

"Why, right here on this mountain you can find God's intentions. He made the world tough, that's the truth. There's bristle-cone pine on Mt. Princeton, right up there at timberline, that've been there for four thousand years — four thousand years of cold and heat, freezing wind and blazing sun. Those tough little trees are part of God's creation. They were there two thousand years before Christ came to give us another chance. The whole world cries out to God's presence. When we grab hold of that truth, we're really free. Not bad for an old sheepherder, huh?"

The fire had died down. Only the mountain hung over our darkened camp. The sheep were bedded down, the dog dozed by the coals with one eye cocked open. Everything seemed all right with our little bit of the world that night.

The sheepherder is long gone, but I remember that night as though it were yesterday.

Gas Creek

Another of my favorites was Georgie House. Mrs. House was the schoolteacher at Gas Creek, the little red-brick schoolhouse out in the valley. She taught all eight grades and put a couple of generations of ranch kids through school. In 1941 Mrs. House lost her husband in an accident on the D & RG and needed a job to support herself. She had only a year and a half of college, but teachers of any kind were scarce during the war, so the ranchers on the school board wangled an "emergency certificate" to clear the way for hiring Mrs. House.

Gas Creek had a teacher, and a good one. She taught those kids how to read and write and figure. She taught the big ones to take care of the little ones. She taught them all to respect her authority — and she never gave them a bum steer. She walked back and forth between school and her little house down the road and never — I mean never — let the winter weather close Gas Creek. If the kids could get there through the drifts, they could bank on Mrs. House's being there. She had an old-fashioned virtue called character and she taught her kids what was expected of them. Quite a lady, that raw-boned old farm girl; quite a lady.

When the war was over, the two-bit bureaucrats in Denver started cracking down on the wartime "emergency certificates." They told Mrs. House she'd have to go back to

school in the summers and work on her college degree. She went down to Adams State Teachers College in the San Luis Valley the next summer and came back so damn mad she could hardly talk.

"I spent the whole summer sitting in class with sweet young things without a brain in their heads. They were too busy looking for their boyfriends to pay any attention to school.

"The teachers weren't much better. I've forgotten more about teaching reading than that young professor ever knew. Why, I never heard such nonsense in my life. That kid with the steamy glasses who was supposed to be teaching reading techniques doesn't believe in phonics. *He doesn't believe in phonics!* Well, I hope he and Dick and Jane and Spot are very happy together. They deserve one another.

"I'll tell you this: I'm not going back there next summer or any other summer. As long as you want me to teach at Gas Creek, I'll stay, but I'll stay and do what I do best — teach youngsters. If you want a college education for the job, you'll have to get somebody else."

The ranchers pulled a few strings in Denver and kept Mrs. House on at Gas Creek. Every few years, they'd have to fight again, but they always won. Mrs. House stayed on at Gas Creek for nearly thirty years and taught the next generation of kids to respect themselves.

When she retired to live in that little house looking up at the mountains, Mrs. House raised her flowers, caught up on her reading, and was always home to one or another of the many Gas Creek alumni who stopped by. She kept that little house, woodstove and all, as clean as a pin.

When she came to town with what proved to be a fatal heart attack, she walked into the hospital a little slowly, but erect and in charge as always. She said, "I think I've had a heart attack. Will you please look into it."

She had indeed. The nurse couldn't find a pulse. "Please lay down, Mrs. House."

"Wilma Boomershine, you mean *lie* down. Didn't you learn anything at Gas Creek?"

Mrs. House died a couple of hours later, but she and Gas Creek are still there for many of us in this valley.

Called or Not, God Is Present

I remember so many of them — so tough, so loyal, so real. Sometimes it seems they're still here. Once in a while in town I see a face on the street that brings me up short. "Why, isn't that . . . " No, it isn't, of course. Sometimes it's the daughter or the granddaughter of a face from the past. More often, it's just my memory playing tricks. Either way, that's when you realize with a start that you're really getting old.

I knew for sure how old I had become when I started waking in the middle of the night with that strange feeling of being half in and half out of my body. At that moment, when you can feel yourself in that old body and at the same moment look down on yourself, the bed, and the room as a sort of disinterested observer, you realize that another presence has joined you. Death is standing next to the bed.

Sensing that night visitor isn't frightening. Somehow the experience brings with it a sense of how very beautiful our world is. To have been an infinitesimal particle of God's purpose is so beautiful and so complete that everything finds explanation and fulfillment in that purpose. You feel not so much that you've come home, as that you had never left. God's always been there — in all those wonderful people, in all the beautiful earth itself.

Most of us are too busy to know that, of course. I was caught between the nineteenth century and the twentieth century — and there never was a more busy, self-important age. Much of the nineteenth century was pioneer and frontier, self-reliance and courage, Grammaw Hagee and Grampa Stewart. They lived in a time and a place where you had to be tough and loyal to your friends — and yet be prepared ultimately to go it alone.

Along toward the end of the century, the passing frontier got all mixed up with another nineteenth-century idea — progress. Wealth was "just around the corner." Well, the "wealth" and the "progress" came, but the oldtimers and some of the next generation were never convinced that things were better off.

I've seen countless changes in my life and I've never been certain that I liked them all. You've got to be careful, God may give you what you ask for.

Now that I'm nearing graduation day, I think I've finally figured out that it doesn't make much difference. The important part of all this is people — families, loyalty, love, courage. People. Reflections of the face of God.

VIII

POSTSCRIPT

I'm Gibby Gregg, the country editor George told you
about.

When I stopped by the cabin to check on George, I
found him dead. I also found this journal just as you've
read it. I was as close to George as anyone, I guess — but
I never knew the journal existed. Never once had he even
mentioned it. When I realized what I was holding, I built
up the fire and sat in that tiny cabin, surrounded with
snowy silence, and read every word of it. I'm sure George
was still there with me.

He didn't tell all the stories. I know he had many more
to tell. But I don't believe he ran out of time. He just
decided that some things aren't anybody's business. He was
writing about people who were looking for something.
Some thought they had found it, others kept looking.
George was one of those who found what he was looking
for.

In the process, he told a little piece of history, not the kind you learn in school about wars and presidents and economic trends and the rest. His history was about a few people he knew and loved, about the mountains they all loved, about how they saw themselves and their country, about another time and place that meant something to him. He was writing the history of the country he knew, because it made a difference to him and he didn't want it forgotten.

Mostly, I believe he was writing about his discovery of God — or maybe God's discovery of George. One day he looked up and saw the face of God and realized He had been there all along — in the people and the country he loved.

There was something special between George and his Maker, something each of us must discover for himself.

George has gone home now.

*   *   *   *   *

All which thy child's mistake
Fancies as lost, I have stored for Thee at home.

The Hound of Heaven

MT. SHAVANO   MT. ANTERO   MT. PRINCETON

THE CABIN

MARY MURPHY MINE

CHALK CREEK GULCH

THE BIG HOTEL

CHALK CREEK

GAS CREEK SCHOOL

BUE

SALIDA

ARKANSAS RIVER

NORTH